The Notebooks of

MAJOR THOMPSON

by Pierre Daninos

TRANSLATED BY ROBIN FARN

Illustrated by Walter Goetz

1955: ALFRED · A · KNOPF

NEW YORK

The Notebooks of
MAJOR
THOMPSON

AN ENGLISHMAN DISCOVERS

FRANCE & THE FRENCH

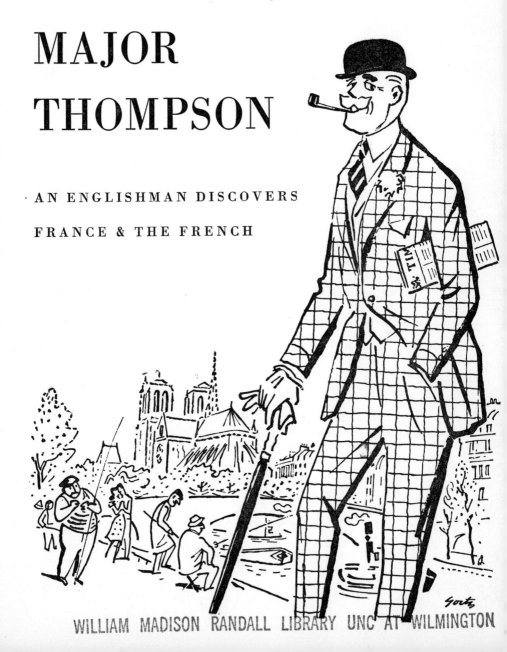

L. C. catalog card number: 55–9259

© *Alfred A. Knopf, Inc., 1955*

THIS IS A BORZOI BOOK,
PUBLISHED BY ALFRED A. KNOPF, INC.

Published September 19, 1955
Second printing, October 1955
Third printing, November 1955

ORIGINALLY PUBLISHED *in France as* Les Carnets du Major Thompson. *Copyright by Librairie Hachette 1954. Published in Great Britain by Jonathan Cape, Ltd. under the title of* Major Thompson Lives in France.

SOME OF THE ILLUSTRATIONS *by Walter Goetz are reproduced with the kind permission of* Punch.

Contents

The Notebooks of

MAJOR THOMPSON

The Notebooks

MAY I INTRODUCE MYSELF?

No well-brought-up Englishman (if I may be permitted such redundancy without offense to my honorable countrymen) can, without loss of dignity, talk about himself, especially at the beginning of a story. But, like space travelers who when they reach a certain height are no longer subject to the laws of gravitation, once landed on the Continent I no longer feel bound by the laws of British gravity. And as I am to talk about people to whom I have never been formally introduced, I feel rather more free in doing what is not done—that is, in giving information about myself which in England would seem uncalled for.

My name is Thompson.

William Marmaduke Thompson.

Having had the good fortune to be born an Englishman, I go forward in life sandwichwise, preceded by my initials and followed by the little cushion whereon national honors have, with the passing of years, added their alluvial deposit.

W. M. Thompson, C.S.I., D.S.O., O.B.E.

It is hard to conceive how precious these little letters fore and aft are to an Englishman. They are the inviolable frontiers of his person; they protect him like a Guardsman's waterproof from too direct human contacts. When a Frenchman sends me a letter addressed simply to "Monsieur Thompson" I feel as if I had caught cold in my surname and been undressed in public. This is especially annoying because it is, after all, the sender who is in the wrong and I who feel I am giving offense.

I should not wish the French to take this remark amiss. If I venture to talk about them frankly, it is because I love them every bit as much as they love the Queen of England. Could anyone love them more than that? After I left the Army and Ursula had passed

4

THOMPSON, MAJOR HON. WILLIAM MARMADUKE, *C.S.I.* (*1934*), *D.S.O.* (*1943*), *O.B.E.* (*1931*). b. Oct. 8, 1902. *4th s. of 4th Earl Strawforness.* Education: *Rugby; Trinity College, Fellow of All Souls, Oxford.* Married: *I. 1929 Penelope Ursula Hopkins (1931); II. 1932 Martine-Nicole Noblet. Entered Army 1924, served Waziristan Campaign (1924), transferred to India, Rawalpindi District (1926), 9th Lancers Mesopotamia, (1928), 38th Dogras Palestine and Egypt (1931). Secretary to the Hon. the Political Resident, Persian Gulf (1931). Political Agent, Kuwait (1932). Served* 2nd World War *1939-1945 with Royal Warwickshire Regt. (dispatches twice, D.S.O., Croix de Guerre). Ret. from Army 1945. Member H.M. Diplomatic Service.* Publication: The Arab of Mesopotamia; *various communications on the South African lepidoptera.* Recreations: *big-game hunting, natural history, golf, gardening.* Clubs: *Cavalry (London), Automobile Club (Paris), Honorable Company of Edinburgh Golfers (Muirfield).* Addresses: *England: Tower Cottage, Rowlands Castle, Pendleton, Hampshire. Continent: c/o Thos. Cook & Son, Paris.*

away,[1] I made my home in Paris, in the country of my second wife, so that I feel doubly privileged: I am an Englishman nourished *à la française.*

The many sports along with which I pursued my studies (without ever seeming really to catch up with them) did not develop me physically any more than is usually the case with my compatriots. I am fairly tall, and highly colored in complexion. The slight parentheses of my legs betray the horseman. My eyes are blue and round, and my perpetual state of astonishment has gradually made them quite prominent (especially since I have been living in France). My nose stops short and looks as if there had not been quite enough time to finish it; my rounded cheeks glow like Canadian apples, whose ruddiness, together with the bluish line of my temples and the white bar of my mustache, make my face a living replica of the British flag.

I may add that my front teeth, which project slightly

---

[1] Expression which the English prefer to the word "die," especially when speaking of someone dear to them. Ursula was the Major's first wife.

over my lower lip, make the unsuspecting (who are few in England, where this malformation is rather common) believe that I am always laughing and am even more jovial than my appearance would lead them to imagine.

But I must get down to speaking of the chief source of astonishment in my life, which is the very subject of these notes.

Now, I know this will appear incredible, and yet, by Saint George, it is the unvarnished truth: India's sun has bronzed my skin; for the welfare of Her Most Gracious Majesty I have roasted in the burning sands of Mesopotamia; the Intelligence (which in Great Britain is more keenly appreciated as a branch of the Service than as a quality) has sent me to execute highly confidential missions in Bechuanaland, in Palestine, and among the Afghans. And yet I may honestly say today that never have I felt so far from home as now, twenty-one miles from Dover, in this fair land which bears the gentle name of France.

May the rampant beasts on the Royal Standard tear me to shreds if I am lying: I feel nearer to London in the Caiman Islands than in Angoulême, and the customs of the Maori warriors seem to me less mysterious than the habits of a burgher of Roubaix. Astonishing as it seems, the Almighty allowed himself only a few bucketfuls of water to separate the two most dissimilar peoples on earth.

In short, at a time when the whole world appears to be caught up in the madness of exploration, and muddled by the heights of the Himalayas or by the depths of the Pacific, it seems to me rather urgent to discover France.

P.S.   I owe my thanks for his meritorious efforts to my friend and collaborator, P. C. Daninos, who is naturally distressed that he is not English—that would have been his only chance of acquiring some sense of humor. As it is, he is reduced to the humble task of editing these notebooks. May he never betray me! That is what I hope for but can scarcely expect. When people have been hereditary enemies for so long, something always sticks in the subconscious. Moreover, he has been speaking English for a mere twenty years and already thinks he knows it. It would be equally presumptuous on my part to claim that because I have been associating with French people for a quarter of a century I know them. The only people who claim to know such a country inside and out are those who have crossed it in two weeks and left with a ready-made opinion unopened in their suitcase. Those who live there learn each day that they know nothing about it, except perhaps the opposite of what they knew already.

Chapter 1

WHAT IS A FRENCHMAN?

One day, in the secrecy of his Harley Street office, a friend of mine who is a famous brain surgeon opened up an Englishman.

He discovered the following: one of Her Majesty's battleships, a mackintosh, a royal crown, a cup of tea, a bobby, the Rules and Regulations of the Royal and Ancient Golf Club of St. Andrews, a Coldstream Guard, a bottle of whisky, a Bible, the Calais-Mediterranean timetable, a nurse from Westminster Hospital, a cricket ball, some fog, a bit of earth upon which the sun never sets, and—at the very bottom of his lawn-covered subconscious—a cat-o'-nine-tails and a black-stocking school-girl.

Conscious of having committed an unpardonable indiscretion, rather than appalled by his discovery, he called neither Scotland Yard nor the Vice Squad; he closed him up again. And the doctor was obliged to admit that all this went into the making of a really good Englishman.

I have often wondered what my friend would find if he opened up a Frenchman.[1]

By Jove! How can you define a Frenchman?

The accepted definition of the Frenchman as one who eats bread and knows no geography and wears the Legion of Honor in his buttonhole is not altogether in-

wwwwwwwwwwwwww

[1] A South African girl, having read about the Major's problem in her newspaper, wrote to the *Natal Daily News* of Durban, which on January 20, 1954 published this curious reply: "I know the surgeon in question and can confirm the Major's statement. I was the nurse, and saw the different objects being brought out. What the Major does not relate is that the surgeon was French, and what he does not know is that I fell in love with him. One day he himself underwent a brain operation. To the general amazement, when his skull was opened there were found nineteen Presidents of the Council, three dancers from the Folies-Bergère, half a box of ripe Camembert, a complete Maginot Line, and several lorry loads of devaluated francs."

accurate (although when you look more closely at the Legion of Honor it often turns out to be the Order of Ouissam Alaouite); but it does not go far enough.

I am alarmed by the thought[2] that if my friend were to open a Frenchman he would be seized with dizziness and fall into an abyss of contradictions.

Really! How can you define these people who spend their Sundays proclaiming themselves republicans and the rest of the week worshiping the Queen of England, who call themselves modest yet always talk about being the torch-bearers of civilization, who treat their common sense as one of their principal exports while keeping so little of it for themselves that they overthrow governments almost before they are set up, who keep their hearts in France and their fortunes abroad, who are enemies of Jews in general but intimately friendly with them in particular, who love to

[2] A turn of phrase belonging to the same category as the famous "I'm afraid" so dear to the English: for example, when an Englishman knows quite well that he has forgotten something, he says he is very much afraid he has forgotten it. And if a woman who has just seen her husband set off for his office has to answer a phone call for him, she will generally say: "I'm afraid he's out."

hear their comedians make fun of retired army officers but who come to attention at the first sound of a bugle, who detest having their failings exposed but constantly speak ill of themselves, who say they love purity of line but cherish an affection for the Eiffel Tower, who respect the Englishman's ignorance of petty maneuvering but would think it ridiculous to declare the real amount of their income to the tax-collector, who revel in stories of Scotch thrift but will always try to buy at a price lower than the one marked, who loathe crossing a frontier without smuggling something just to be doing it but dislike not being legally *"en règle,"* who are anxious to proclaim that you cannot "take them" but who rush to elect a deputy who promises them the moon, who wear winter clothing throughout April but shut off their heating-systems on March 31, who vaunt the charms of their countryside but cover it with architectural monstrosities, who have a marked respect for the law courts but never go to a lawyer except to find out how to get around the law, and finally, who are delighted when one of their great men talks to them of their *greatness,* their *great* civilizing mission, their *great* country, their *great* traditions, but who dream of nothing except to retire, after a pleasant *little* life, to a quiet *little* corner, on a *little* piece of land of their own, with a *little* wife who will be satisfied with inexpensive *little* dresses, concoct nice *little* dishes, and on occasion be ready to receive her husband's friends charmingly when they come for a *little* game of cards.

These conservatives who for two hundred years have not stopped slipping over to the left, these republicans who for more than a century have suppressed their royalty and taught their children, with voices choked with emotion, the history of the kings who created France—how can a poor devil of an observer define them except in terms of contradiction.

A Frenchman? A being who is, above all, a contradiction of what you think he is.

If I were obliged to determine the dominant feature of a Frenchman's character, I would say it is skepticism.

My old friend M. Taupin says that he is much attached to republican institutions, yet if a deputy closes

The Frenchman's dream

his speech with an appeal to the great principles of 1789, Taupin smiles ironically. It is clear that he no longer believes in them. M. Taupin is a convinced partisan of peace. Yet when the representatives of the Great Powers meet around a table to attempt to establish what the press calls "the basis for world accord" and subsequently publish a communiqué that proves the *identity of their points of view,* Taupin smiles again, shakes his head, and says to me:

"You don't mean to say you believe *that?* Pfuittt! It's always the same—just words!"

Invaded, occupied, oppressed, bullied, dragging memories of the turn of the century and the gold standard behind him, M. Taupin is a man who does not believe in anything because, in his opinion, it no longer serves any purpose to believe in anything.

It happens sometimes that after the English have hesitated for a long time they do something. As they think little and reflect even less, they do believe in it.

The French do not believe in what they do. Take the Chamber of Deputies. It looks as if they manufactured deputies just to have them there to throw out. If

I ride with M. Taupin in a bus past the Chamber, his face lights up with a sarcastic smile.

Is he a royalist? No.

Bonapartist? Not that either.

Does he long for a dictatorship? He has a horror of dictatorships.

So—?

He is a moderate whose revolutionary spirit is limited to requiring him to vote radical, or, if he is really in a bad temper, radical-socialist. Perhaps just as our bus is passing the Chamber the very member elected by M. Taupin is invoking the sacred principles of 1789 and the Rights of Man. And yet this public servant does not believe in them any longer. M. Taupin declares that a man is not the same man once he has taken his seat with six hundred others. Perhaps he is right. In any case, it is clear that he looks upon his representatives with small goodwill—rather, with that same regard which we reserve for the usurper who dares flaunt a black tie with narrow blue stripes when he has never attended Eton. And it is plain from their expressions that his neighbors think as he does. It is hard to believe that the passengers of this bus sent to the Chamber the members who sit there. They seem to belong to two different planets.

Generally the situation is summed up by a gentleman wearing a decoration:

"What we need is a strong man who would clean things up a bit in there. A good sweeping out."

You might suppose that these people were hoping for a dictator. Wrong. Let the strong man appear on the horizon, let him talk about reforming institutions, restoring order, establishing discipline, and for every hopeful voter you have a thousand up in arms. He is a traitor and a scoundrel. He wants to butcher the Republic. An artillery of republican slogans is rolled out, 1789 is invoked, and this date which only a moment before made M. Taupin laugh now makes him very grave.

An impartial observer might be tempted to believe that what the French have most at heart is universal suffrage, the expression of the will of the people, republican institutions—in a word, the Chamber. But you have only to pass by in a bus—(see above)

.　　.　　.

It is easy to see that, given these conditions, France is a difficult country to govern. Power slips out of one's hands as soon as it is grasped. Yet foreigners are wrong to criticize the French from this point of view, accusing them of inconstancy. In my view, this, precisely, is a sign of good health. Many countries lose their heads whenever they lose their governments. The French, whose governments are certainly enough to make them lose their heads, have the incomparable virtue of keeping calm on these occasions. France is the only country in the world with a body healthy enough to allow her to live for one month out of every four without a head. With us a government is a necessity; in France it is a luxury which she can offer herself three, four, or five times a year thanks to the soundness of her constitution and her famous common sense, which enables this admirable nation to venture without losing its balance along the most damnably difficult paths.

Chapter 2

SWEET LAND OF MISTRUST—
AND CREDULITY

The French are inclined to believe that other countries live with their eyes fixed on France. At least, that's what their newspapers say. At the slightest crisis they write: "Every day the world is watching us."

As for myself, I must say I rarely take my stand on the cliffs of Dover before daybreak with a telescope to watch how the French arise in the morning![1] I think it

wwwwwwwwwwwww

[1] In French: *se lèvent*. The Major had first written "how they wash" (*se lavent*), but his collaborator pointed out that the French might see herein a hurtful allusion to recent statistics which revealed that the French use in a year only half as much toilet soap as the English do.

would be indecent. No doubt some damned foreigners spend all their time in this fashion.

I used to wonder about this inquisitive foreigner; then I saw him in one of my rare dreams. He had one foot in the Kremlin, the other in Piccadilly; his head was British, his stomach Russian, his subconscious German, his wallet American, his memory filled with Waterloos and Sedans. He was watching fair France with an international and slightly malevolent eye.

The French are convinced that their country wishes no one any harm. The English are condescending, the Americans bossy, the Germans sadistic, the Italians incomprehensible, the Russians impenetrable, the Swiss Swiss. But the French are nice. Other people are horrid to them.

There are two possibilities for France. To dominate the world by her Radiant Influence (territorial conquests, development in Arts and Letters, etc.)—such are the great heroic epochs of ascendant France. Or, on the other hand, to be invaded and conquered. Then France is trodden underfoot, massacred, crucified. Such are the great heroic epochs of downfallen France.

The first condition satisfies France's pride and thirst for greatness. This is her Napoleonic side. From the second she draws her irresistible force of recovery. This is her Joan of Arc side.

It is difficult for a Frenchman to imagine that anyone can honestly see France otherwise than with an olive branch in hand, a tender prey at the mercy of bellicose nations. Any honest observer must admit that this state of mind is fairly legitimate, since three times in less than a century France has had to suffer the most savage onslaughts of the Teuton race. Still, if he can back off far enough to make an impartial judgment and, disregarding the records of the last eighty years (mere grains of dust in history's hourglass), study the annals of earlier centuries, he must admit that a Spaniard whose town was sacked by Napoleon's armies finds it somewhat difficult to look upon France as an innocent victim. Foreigners should, however, realize that when a French army goes into the Palatinate or into Saragossa, it does not do so on purpose.[2]

~~~~~~~~~~~~~~~~~~~

[2] This passage brought about a lively discussion between the Major and his French collaborator. "Am I to understand that if your

Persecuted by her enemies who make war, by her allies who make peace behind her back, by the whole world which steals her inventions (the French invent only so as to complain the next minute that the invention has been stolen), the Frenchman also feels persecuted by the French: by the government which makes a fool of him, by the Treasury which makes him pay too many taxes, by his boss who pays him too little for his work, by businessmen who make fortunes at his expense, by his neighbor who slanders him—in short, by *tout le monde.*

This menace which he believes is continually driving him to the wall mobilizes him into a permanent state of *self-defense.* This comes out clearly when two Frenchmen ask about each other. In other countries people get on well, or badly, but somehow they get on. In France *"on se défend"*—"they defend themselves."

The average Frenchman's "I'm defending myself as

<hr />

revered ancestor Major Raikes Hodson, in the name of His Most Gracious Majesty, with his own hand puts to death the three sons of the King of India and sends the King himself to die in exile at Rangoon, it's all for their good?" "In a way, yes, definitely," said the Major.

2 3

well as I can" is the mark of a man who lives in a perpetual state of siege.

Yet who menaces the amiable Frenchman? A very short word in his vocabulary to which my friend and collaborator was good enough to draw my attention disclosed the secret identity of the assailants: the word is *They*. And *They* are simply everybody: for employees the bosses, for bosses employees, for masters servants, and for servants masters, for pedestrians motorists or for motorists pedestrians, and for all of them the great common enemies: the State, the Treasury, and the foreigner.

Surrounded by enemies as England is by water, harassed by insatiable marauders who envy him his lovely country, his wallet, his freedom, his rights, his honor, his wife, it is easy to see that the Frenchman must be always on his guard.

He is mistrustful.

Could I say he is born mistrustful, grows up mistrustful, marries mistrustfully, makes a career of mistrust, and dies even more mistrustful because, like timid people who sometimes have fits of audacity, he has sometimes been the victim of disastrous spells of credulity? I think I could.

What exactly is the Frenchman mistrustful of?

Of everything.

From the moment he sits down in a restaurant M. Taupin—who lives in the country whose people eat the best food in the world—begins to be mistrustful of what he is about to be served.

Oysters, yes.

"But," says he to the waiter, "are they really good? You guarantee them?"

I have never yet heard a waiter answer: "No, I can't guarantee them!" He might be heard to say: "They are good—but"—leaning confidentially toward his customer—"not your sort, M. Taupin (or M. Deletange-Delbet, or M. Dupont)"—which, of course, especially if M. Taupin has a friend with him, amounts to a twenty-one-gun salute.

M. Taupin knows very well that if oysters figure on the menu, it is because they are fresh, but he likes to be reassured, and, above all, he does not want to be taken for a man whose leg can be pulled.

M. Taupin mistrusts even the water. He calls for fresh water as if there were also carafes of warm or polluted water available; and he wants fresh bread, and wine that is not cut.

"Is your Pomerol decent? Drinkable? Not just swill, I trust?"

Good Lord! What would happen in a country like mine, where sitting down to a meal can *really* be such a horrible adventure!

Having had a good (little) dinner, M. Taupin does some mental arithmetic over the bill.

"It's the principle of the thing," he says, fearful of being cheated. If he fails to find a mistake, he seems disappointed. If he does spot one, he is furious. After which he leaves, more mistrustful than ever.

Some time ago when Taupin and I were riding to the Austerlitz Station on our way to a little town in the South West, he said he needed to stop at a pharmacy and buy some medicine.

"Too bad. Don't you feel well?" I asked.

"It isn't that, but I'm suspicious of Gascon food."

"It's the principle of the thing"

"Couldn't you buy the medicine when you get there?"

"You never know in those little towns. I'll feel better if I buy it in Paris."

To my great surprise, our taxi drove past a number of pharmacies that looked like quite decent pharmacies, but M. Taupin seemed to have no faith in any of them. And then I understood the meaning of that phrase which had always puzzled me: "On sale at all good pharmacies." Those we had passed were evidently the others.

At last he found a good one. As he returned to the taxi clasping a small bottle, he said apologetically: "I don't trust these drugs, they don't do any good anyway. But my wife believes in them. There's nothing like faith."

As we approached the station M. Taupin seemed nervous and kept glancing at his watch. Finally he asked the driver for the *right* time. An Englishman or a German says: "What's the time?" "*Wieviel Uhr ist es?*" And he is told the time. But M. Taupin would not be satisfied with any ordinary time. He wants the *right* time —Greenwich time, observatory time, Mount Palomar time. On this occasion he seemed reassured by the taxi-driver's time, though it was scarcely different from his own. But once inside the station, he made a final verification in the waiting room because, as he explained to me, clocks outside stations are always kept running three minutes faster than the inside ones to hurry up the travelers. So M. Taupin set his watch three minutes behind station time and a minute fast as a matter of principle, which in the end made him lose at least sixty seconds.

We settled into two corner seats. Then we got out to stroll on the platform, but first Taupin held three seats with his hat, his umbrella, and my mackintosh.

"There are only two of us," I said.

"It's safer," he said. "People are so pushy."

I thought M. Taupin had no doubts about the train: he had consulted the timetable. But catching sight of an official, he inquired:

"We don't change, do we? You're sure?" And turning to me: "These timetables! I don't trust them."

There's nothing like a train for bringing out the *They* hydra. I expected that, but this time I had more than I could take. The monster seemed to be in a state of torpor in the general somnolence, when suddenly toward the end of this dark, cold day the electric lights in our car dimmed.

"They might at least," piped a little old lady of seventy with a foot-warmer, "inspect their compartments before putting them into service." Up till then the five other French people in the compartment, taciturn, mistrustful, and reserved, had been quietly reading their newspapers or those of their neighbors. (*"May I? . . . Thank you so much!"*) No doubt they were only waiting for a signal—or, rather, the *They* sign—to dash into the fray. The *They*, like a football, was at once captured by a prosperous-looking woman wearing a heavy veil and a small dog (*"And to think they made me take a ticket for this poor little animal!"*), only to be caught in the air and converted into a try for a goal by the right wing, a gentleman obviously very sure of himself, traveling under the protection of the Legion of Honor rosette, a gold watch chain, and a triple chin, all of which was bouncing with his sardonic laughter.

"So long as they make us pay!"

"To hell with everything else!"

The battle had become general. An old sporting instinct made me regret not taking part in it. But in my role of silent arbiter I merely checked the score and counted the *They's*.

"If they gave us a government—"

"There is one, but there might as well not be."

"What we need is a government that governs."

"You're asking too much!"

"A man with a firm hand—"

"I'd throw them all out—a clean sweep!"

"Meanwhile, there they are!"

"That's right. Sitting there—"

"All they think of is loading their pockets."

"Grease the palm! Jobs for the boys!"

"And their travel paid by the state. Did you see about that so-called parliamentary mission to Darkest Africa? Who pays for all that, if you'd mind telling me?"

"We do!"

"You do!"

"I do."

"Of course! No, they are going too far this time. Shameful! Our wonderful country!"

"So rich!"

"And only asking to get on its feet."

"They'll end by ruining it—"

"They're capable of that!"

"Look at this compartment! Isn't it a scandal? When I think of foreigners traveling! What must they think?" (All eyes turn toward me, asking for pardon— "May England forgive us!")

"I shall write to the Company."

"You can write—they won't even read your letter."

As the ticket-inspector happened to be passing at that moment, the lady with the little dog opened fire on him: "It's a scandal, do you hear, a scandal! You ought to refund my ticket money!"

"If you have a claim to make, madame," says the Inspector, "you must write to the S.N.C.F."

"Then you, what are you supposed to be for?"

"I look after the tickets, madame—your ticket, please."

The gentleman with the Legion of Honor, who was burning to intervene, threw himself into the melee. "I must ask you to be civil to the lady!"

"I am civil, sir, and, anyway, who asked you? Your ticket, please!"

"All right, I won't show it!"

"We'll see about that. If you want to start something—"

"That's enough! You'll pay for that, my friend.[3] First of all"—pulling out a gold pencil on a chain—"let me have your number." He drew himself up to the level of the Inspector's head, adjusting his spectacles and licking his pencil. "Three thousand nine hundred and eighty-seven. Good! Well, three thousand nine hundred eighty-seven can just wait. Here, take my ticket—and you'll get a good deal more than that from me, my friend, lots more!"

The Inspector smiled, quite calm, and—*click-clack!* —punched the ticket.

"He who laughs last laughs best," said M. Rosette.

"Meanwhile, tickets, please!"

Grumbling, the travelers reluctantly complied. When the Inspector had gone, the lady with the dog

[3] When a Frenchman calls another Frenchman "my friend," it is a sure sign that he considers him already his enemy (*Major's note*).

hissed through her veil: "Tss! What a mentality! You never saw that before the War! And they're all the same!"

"Or worse, madame!"

"It just shows you!"

A few moments later when I went out into the corridor to get some air, I heard the Inspector tell a colleague who had joined him:

"I don't know what's the matter with them all today. I wouldn't touch them with a ten-foot pole. Watch out for yourself."

Inspectors mistrustful of travelers, travelers mistrustful of inspectors—who on this French train, this mistrusting train, was most mistrustful?

I was still pondering this when we arrived at our destination. Need I say that M. Taupin displayed his mistrust the moment he arrived at the hotel? Especially about the beds. He poked them, felt the sheets, inspected the wardrobe. I do not think this mistrust was peculiar to him. Millions of Frenchmen are mistrustful of hotel-keepers, bills, oysters, of the women who lead them by the nose, of the army men who push them forward, the politicians who hold them back, the anti-militarists who would sell France to the first comer, the schoolteachers who stuff the minds of their children, of their enemies, their friends, and, secretly, of themselves.

Chapter 3

THE REALM OF SUBDIVISION

France is divided into forty three million Frenchmen.

France is the only country in the world where if you add ten citizens to ten citizens you have not made an addition—you have made twenty divisions.

It would be much more in Freud's line than in an English major's to show why it is that these guillotiners of kings, who are everlastingly divided against themselves, dream of Buckingham Palace and of a unified France, which has come to be thought of as the one panacea for all her wounds. A war, at least, is necessary to apply this prescription, which then goes by the name of Sacred Union. The French at once call up a hundred and fifty divisions. We cannot complain about that. No longer able to fight with one another, they fight a common enemy, and allow us English time, according to our traditions, to *wait* a little longer *and see* a little more.

When peace returns, France resumes battle. In the shade of buildings inscribed with the words Equality and Fraternity, she devotes herself freely to one of her favorite sports (almost as popular as bicycle-racing): class warfare. As I do not wish to compete with the experts, I shall leave it to them to explain the evolution of this sport throughout the ages, its rules and its trends. One thing, however, does strike me: the American pedestrian who sees a millionaire going past in a Cadillac dreams secretly of the day when he will be driving his own; the French pedestrian who sees a millionaire going past in a Cadillac dreams of the day he will get him out of it and make him walk like everybody else.[1]

As for enumerating all the divisions that separate

---

[1] It will be noticed that the Major carefully avoids speaking of the English pedestrian, who is, of course, too well bred to dream things in the street.

Frenchmen, I give up. Only one thing: for every Frenchman who wakes up as a nudist in Port-de-Bouc, you may be perfectly certain that another Frenchman will arise an anti-nudist in Malo-les-Bains.

You might think the antagonism would end there. Hardly. The nudist founds an organization, which elects an Honorary President (himself) and a Vice President. Then the Vice President, having quarreled with the aforesaid President, forms a neo-nudist Committee rather more leftish than the first one. For his part, the anti-nudist, having taken the chair at an Honorary committee . . . etc.

The same process holds as true for politics as it does for skiing. The fashion for short skis has just been launched. Immediately the entire skiing world of France has splintered into an anti-short and anti-long. In the heart of every Frenchman there slumbers an *anti* ready to awaken at the approach of the slightest *pro*. This explains the inextricable puzzle of French political groups. How can a normally constituted Englishman—that is to say, one just barely able to understand the difference between Conservative and Labor—appreciate those essential nuances that separate a Leftist Republican from a Republican of the Left, or a deputy of the Republican and Social Action Union from a deputy of the Republican and Social Action Party? I can't, really.

As I am incapable of examining the hundreds of thousands of divisions among Frenchmen (who, as is well known, hate hair-splitting), I will content myself with studying the difference that daily divides France into two camps: officials who tell you that they are always being misused or overlooked; non-officials who claim that all the trouble is caused by the officials.

The result is that every day except Sunday—the day of truce, when the French frankly confess they are bored —forty-two million citizens are arrayed against the forty-third.

At first sight this numerical inferiority seems to condemn the officials. But you must never judge things at first sight in France. Fresh mysteries are always coming to light. In the end you understand with extraordinary clarity why these people are so incomprehensible.

The citizen who ventures into a police station or

into a savings bank or a Town Hall puts me in mind of a bowman setting out for the Hundred Years' War. Armed with a bad disposition and outfitted with a quiverful of sarcastic rejoinders, he is quite certain in advance that he will not get his way, that he will be sent from Bureau 223 on the mezzanine floor to Guichet B on the third floor, from the third floor to the police station, from the police station to the Prefecture, where he learns that a new bylaw dispenses with the necessity for producing the certificate he thought he had to have, in favor of a new one which is the same as the old one except that it requires fresh formalities.

Vis-à-vis this assailant—to whom the administrative vocabulary, as if anxious to put him at a disadvantage from the start, gives the name of *postulant,* or applicant —is the official employee. Generally he is swathed in a colorless sort of overall over a suit he puts on only because he wants to wear it out.

Against this wall of indifference (*"I've seen other people too—if you think you're the only one. I don't make the regulations."*) the arrows of the most bellicose attackers become one by one ineffective. (*"You'll hear from*

me again, my friend! I've a long arm.") The long-armed
gentleman produces from his pocketbook a card with a
red line across it, which no one has time to look at, but
which produces its effect upon the other applicants.
They imagine the gentleman's long arm reaching over
the little official's head, piercing the office walls, crossing
the Seine, making its way into the office of the Minister,
who promptly sacks the delinquent official.

Sheltered behind his grille, the official maintains
his calm: over the assailant he has that advantage
which people seated in a café have over the passers-by.
There is the matter of home ground. He feels himself all
the more in his element for having made a little box (or,
in the case of the women officials, a little basket) in
which he keeps his little belongings: scissors, knitting,
buns, sweets, and sometimes that little rubber stamp
hunted for everywhere and found, by accident, in its
right place.

It may be because my letters are often destined for
distant countries, but the stamps never amount to a
round sum: the young lady tells me I have to pay 93 or
112 or 187 francs, and if she finds without too much

"You'll hear from me again, my friend! I've a long arm!"

trouble the first 50-franc and the second 30-franc stamp, she has to hunt all through a colleague's portfolio for the one to make up the sum—though she may, of course, discover it in the famous little box. I have noticed that the women in post offices have a marked predilection for old cigar boxes. Good heavens! Think what a damned long journey a box of Havanas must have taken before ending up as a workbox on the table of an assistant in the post office!

Sometimes the combatants are separated by plate glass perforated at a certain height by a dozen small holes. I used to believe that these holes were made to facilitate the passage of verbal exchanges. Not at all! They are arranged so that the mouths of employee and spluttering applicant are never on the same level. The opponents are therefore reduced to shouting a bit louder. Sometimes a small opening is arranged on a level with the head of the official. That means that the assailant is forced to lower his, and this movement at once places him in an inferior position.

Through these slits, holes, and gratings the Frenchman devotes a precious part of his existence to proving that he does exist, that he really does live where he lives, and that, as they are not yet deceased, his children are alive.

You might think that if a Frenchman is not dead he is alive. Wrong! In the eyes of the administration he is not alive. He must first have a birth certificate, then a life certificate, sometimes both. (It is true that lately the life certificate has been replaced by a certificate of non-decease.)

If, for example, a Frenchman is planning to go to Italy and needs a passport, then he must proceed to prove a great deal more than the fact that he is alive. Strange as it may appear, a Frenchman's journey to Italy begins in his concierge's room. The concierge can deliver to him without delay—or later on, according to how he feels—the "certificate of domicile" he needs. The adult Frenchman cannot by himself certify that he inhabits the house he lives in. For that he must have verification by his concierge. After that, he will have plenty of time to exhume old memories while he searches for his military-service book, which is rarely in the place he left it ten years ago.

Some while back I met M. Taupin on his way to the police station. He needed a new identity card. A naïve observer would imagine that, as M. Taupin has been well known and respected in his neighborhood for some thirty-five years, he would not need anyone to declare that he really is M. Taupin. Wrong again! In order to declare who he is, M. Taupin must furnish two witnesses. These two witnesses would have to be people who have known him for a long time? Again wrong! The witnesses who have to say they know him do not actually know him at all; but they are known to the Inspector. Generally they keep the local *bistro* or grocer's shop, and by a daily trade in witnessing make something on the side.[2]

Such is the charmingly frank (*la bonne franquette*)

[2] There had been signs of an impending discussion between the Major and his French collaborator, and it flared up at this juncture. The latter having pointed out that the slowness of the English public services was proverbial, and that official indifference there at least equal to that of their French colleagues, the Major said: "Slow, I grant you. *But not indifferent.* Let us say, rather, phlegmatic."

aspect of this fair land, where a smile can soften a gendarme's heart, where you can always discover a loophole in the law by which it can be evaded, and where the strict application of regulations amounts to a sanction. The important thing is the formality. I realized that the minute I set foot in France at Calais, when I heard a disillusioned customs officer with a luscious Auvergnat accent say to a traveler guilty of two infringements:

"If this happens again, I'll have to enforce the regulations."

Chapter 4

THE LAND OF THE HANDSHAKE

For the French—and for many others—England is "the land of the handshake."

M. Taupin, who in spite of what I have told him a hundred times always insists on making me sit in a draft, likewise believes that he must shake hands with great violence because I am English and come from England, the land of the handshake.

Actually, though, the vigorous English handshake is a favorite gesture of French writers who set their detective stories in England to make them seem more real. I think the true land of handshaking is France.

Something like what happened in the case of hand-shaking also happened to table manners. The English have taught the whole world how to behave properly at mealtime; but the French know how to eat. The Anglo-Saxons have discovered a very evocative name for hand-shaking; but the French actually do the shaking. With us this faintly barbaric contact is reduced to a minimum. Once we have shaken hands with someone, he need not expect from us anything else of this nature for the rest of his life.

A statistician in whose calculations I have the ut-most confidence, as he is not a member of any Statistical Society, calculates that a Frenchman of average im-portance, like M. Taupin or M. Charnelet, spends (roughly) half an hour a day (i.e., more than a whole year out of a life of sixty years) shaking hands: at nine o'clock, at twelve, at two, and at six. That, of course, does not include the hands of people he does not know, visitors, relatives, or friends, which would probably raise the annual total to three weeks of handshaking—say, three years out of a lifetime. When we consider that this handshaker spends (roughly) three hours a day at

4 8

table and eight in bed, we must conclude that the Frenchman *lives* (in the English—i.e., correct—meaning of the word) only thirty years out of sixty, which is not enough! [1]

wwwwwwwwwwwwww

[1] A very stormy argument, which at one moment threatened to bring their partnership to an end, now arose between the galloping Major and his somewhat aroused French collaborator.

"Your way of life," said the latter, "is simply deadly!"

"The English," retorted the Major, "prefer to die living in the way they do."

"Why, then, did you come to live in France?"

"That's another story," said the Major. "Anyhow, you must admit that the English waste less time over meals than you do."

"They waste quite enough, when you think what's on their plates!" mused the Frenchman. "And, besides, that's not true. You take three meals a day where we take only two, and statistics prove that you absorb more calories."

"That arises from the recognized fact that our combustibility is first-class."

"And your tea?" inquired the Frenchman.

"What about our tea?" asked the astonished Major.

"Yes, have you calculated that the Englishman who takes his early morning tea at 7 A.M., more tea at breakfast, tea in the office for elevenses, tea at lunch, tea at tea, and finally a cup of tea before he goes to bed, spends (roughly) four years of his life in front of a teapot?"

The Major, who had turned very red, chose to leave the room at this juncture in order to lose his temper in comfortable seclusion. He came back an hour later, calm and having taken his revenge by ingurgitating a cup of his favorite beverage in an *English tearoom* on the rue de Rivoli.

4 9

·   ·   ·

With the French, the technique of shaking hands (which has been standardized in England for the last thousand years) has various nuances: it can be warm, friendly, condescending, cold, evasive, dry. Some people believe they have not really shaken hands unless they have reduced your finger joints to a pulp. Others retain the hold on your hand as if they were loath to give it back to you— use it to emphasize points in their arguments before letting it drop. Some keep your hand warm between both of theirs, some again seem to insinuate a soft, tepid pancake[2] into your palm, which is unpleasant. Others offer you three fingers, or two, or the tip of one. Never mind, they are offering something and you ought to take it. I often see Frenchmen perform miraculous feats of agility right in the middle of heavy traffic in order to transfer to their left hand what they were carrying in their right, and, at the risk of being run over a hundred times, give their right hand to somebody whom this attention leaves quite unmoved, though, occasionally, dead.

[2] The Major, in a desire to smooth over the recent incident, made an elegant concession and originally used the French form *"pannequet."*

Frenchmen perform miraculous feats of agility

The other evening I was watching a dramatic critic finishing off an overdue article his paper was expecting. Some friends came up, hesitated, and then, as though taken by a fit, fell upon him with outstretched hands. They could not help themselves, nor could he.

Five times in five minutes I saw him shake hands with people who said: "Please—don't get up" but who would have thought him "rather distant that evening" if he had not upset all his notes and mislaid his pen in order to bid them good-evening. The French are extremely touchy on this point. Somebody would have remarked at once:

"Why, he didn't shake hands!"

"Queer!"

He would have had to search all through yesterday's events to discover some detail he had forgotten which might have given offense. "He didn't shake hands with me as usual" is just as serious. The supreme affront is not to take a proffered hand, but leave it suspended in mid-air. When a Frenchman says: "I wouldn't take his hand," it is like our saying: "I cut him dead."

·   ·   ·

A foreigner who has lived for some time in France soon acquires the habit of grasping every hand within reach. Now, when I go back to England my forearm is continually reaching out into the void. My compatriots do not know what to do with it. It is easy to extend your hand, but disconcerting to have to withdraw it when nobody wants it. The other day in Grosvenor Square a friendly-looking fellow did take my hand, but, now that I reflect on it, it was probably just an accident, or a foreigner.

Indeed, the little strip of water which separates England from the Continent was not called an "arm of the sea," or "La Manche," for nothing. It is without doubt the frontier of the arm. Twenty-one miles of sea and a hand held out is no longer to be kissed, and the hand that was formerly thrust forth must now be kept still at one's side.

The English, from that tender age when they already appear so hardened to life, learn to live with their elbows close to their sides—on foot, on horseback, at table. Watch an Englishman eating. You can scarcely see his arms move. It looks as if he was not eating (and *can* he be said to eat?), but having his food delivered to his palate by the Intelligence Service. One might diagram the geographical evolution of gestures. It would show that the human arm, motionless at Bournemouth, begins to stir at Calais, is agitated in Paris, and whirls around madly in Rome, where it becomes the actual propeller of one's thought.

It is not only in their way of saying *"bonjour"* that the French appear so strange to their neighbors. What they do next is equally amazing.

When an Englishman meets another Englishman, he says: "How are you?" and is answered: "How are you?"

When a Frenchman meets a Frenchman, he says: "How are you?" and the other immediately begins to give him news of his health.

The British method *seems* perfectly crazy. On reflection, it is perhaps more rational than the French. In the first case, nobody listens to anybody. In the second, with rare exceptions, the first Frenchman does not listen to the other's answer. Either he is in good health and cares little about the health of the other fellow, or else he has a cold and the only thing he cares about is his own cold. For example:

"Still got my sciatica—"

"Ah—sciatica! With me it's all down my left leg. In 1951 I went to a specialist—yes, another one! D'you know what he said? . . ."

And the Frenchman who is suffering from sciatica suffers still more because he has to keep quiet about his 1954 sciatica and listen to the report on the other fellow's 1951 neuritis. It is the same when it comes to a good story—say, of a motor accident or business affairs. One can say in a general way that the French are interested only in those things which have to do with themselves and which are not interesting in other people. Of course, this conversational selfishness is not peculiar to them: one might say the same of other peoples. It would be both true and false. The English are as little interested in their neighbors as the French. But as they do not ask intimate questions about stomach aches, impetigo, or the liver (Private Enemy No. 1 with the French), they do not have to listen to the answer.

Having inquired after their respective healths, that of their relatives and children (*"Snapshots? Aren't they splendid! I must show you mine!"*), the French pass on to the *"Qu'est-ce que vous devenez?"* or "What are you doing now?"

Unlike the English, who never ask such an agonizing question, the French really want to know. So in one minute you must explain that you are not divorced, that you have not moved, and especially if you are—

"Still with the Crédit Lyonnais?"

"Still with the United Insurance?"

"Still with the Oil Company?"

—as if your questioner were astonished you had been kept on so long.

After this stock-taking, during which you bewail your own bad luck and the good luck of others, it is customary to make a rapid return to the health question with: "At all events, you've got your health—that's the main thing anyway (*allez!*)."

The conversation goes on for a bit and finally ends on the no less traditional "I must fly!"—"*Allez, au revoir!*"

I have questioned several natives on this quasi-traditional ritualistic expression, *"Allez!"* Nobody could explain it. I suppose it has something to do with a curious and invisible means of locomotion by which a Frenchman sets off when parting from another Frenchman. Really, most peculiar!

Heavens! I hear the whistle of my teakettle. Sweet call that even the most Francophile Englishman could not resist. I must go attend to it and so shall pause here for a moment. *Allez!*

Chapter 5

APRÈS VOUS

Every French schoolboy knows that at the Battle of Fontenoy the officer commanding the French guards, M. d'Anterroches, advancing alone toward the English, uncovered and cried:

"*Messieurs les Anglais,* fire first!"

Every English schoolboy knows that at the Battle of Fontenoy the officer commanding the English guards, Lord Hay, advancing alone toward the French, uncovered and cried:

"*Messieurs les Français,* fire first!"

As for the experts—divided as they are from birth—they of course disagree. That is their job.

According to some, those words were addressed to the French by one of their leaders, who, on seeing the English emerge from a typically British fog, cried (with this punctuation):

"Messieurs! The English! Fire first!"

Others see here a ruse that was classic at that time: the French strategists may have believed it better to let the enemy use up its first cartridges so as to attack him more easily afterwards.

But many remain faithful to the classic French version of the gallant invitation.

I think it only fair, however, to recall briefly the story of a French on-the-spot witness, the Marquis de Valfons, who wrote: "The English officers having brought their men up to within eighty paces of the French line, halted, dressed the line, and, hat in hand, saluted the French officers, who in their turn uncovered. [Extraordinary, isn't it, with what good manners they knew how to live and die in those days!]

"Then Lord Hay, cane in hand, advanced to within

When battles were fought correctly:

The Gallant Invitation

thirty paces of the French line, uncovered once more, and said to Count d'Anterroches:

" 'Monsieur, give the order to fire,' to which M. d'Anterroches replied: 'No, sir, we never fire first.' "

But someone must have fired first, otherwise there would not have been any Battle of Fontenoy, which would have been just too bad for the experts. Will this honorable company allow an ex-major in the Indian Army to give his view? In my opinion, it is possible—I would not wish to hurt the French—that someone may have called out to Lord Hay's troops: *"Messieurs les Anglais, tirez les premiers!"*

But it is highly improbable that anyone on the English side understood. Everyone knows that, as the whole world is English-speaking, the Englishman's privilege is to understand no language other than his own. And even if he does understand, in no case must he stoop to letting it be known that he does.

An objective study of the truth leads the impartial observer to conclude that this is merely one of those historic sayings invented with the sole aim of helping school children assimilate historical dates and outlines.

The most durable epigrams are generally made of whole cloth. In the present instance, the Fontenoy saying seems to have emerged as one piece from the forges of French history, which specialize in the cold-rolling of such heroic-gallant formulae as "All is lost save our honor," or "Madame, if it be possible it is done, if impossible it shall be done."

With us, the historic enterprise of Birmingham and Leeds, equally renowned for cold-rolling of steel, has also produced a certain style of noble simplicity: "England expects that every man will do his duty" (Nelson before Trafalgar), or in the satirical and haughty saying: "I don't give a twopenny damn what's become of the ashes of Napoleon" (Wellington) or "What France has best taught me is the better appreciation of England" (Johnson).[1]

Both manufactures progress and compete harmlessly. Their products are principally intended for home

[1] The evocation of this saying occasioned a pretty lively sally between the Major and his French collaborator, who remarked pertinently: "One of the things I enjoy most when I travel abroad is the thought that I am going back to France."

consumption. I have never found the French version of Fontenoy in English schoolbooks and I have never found a French history mentioning Wellington's amusing remark.

If I began by speaking of the legend of Fontenoy, it is because it symbolizes so wonderfully, if not the French spirit of gallant courage, at least their desire to possess this spirit. Everyone knows that in battle no one has time to pronounce these charming sayings. The cannon is the language of combatants. Later on, historians invent their speeches.

I should be sorry to think that anyone might see in these remarks an attack on historians. Every man to his trade. And they do theirs wonderfully. My collaborator and friend, M. Daninos, who in the last war was for some time attached as liaison officer to my battalion, told me one day at the height of the retreat from Flanders how sorry he was to be in the thick of the battle. At first I thought (and it made me feel uncomfortable) that he would rather have been at home. But no. What disturbed him was that as a writer he would never be con-

soled for not being able to describe this gigantic en-
counter as well as his colleagues who were not under
fire.

That seems paradoxical, yet it is quite true. The
historian, free from all the tensions that paralyze the
combatant—fear of the N.C.O., or even of the enemy—
is the only one who can take a long view of the conflict,
ignore all the bothersome killing of people, and impart
the necessary color and flexibility to his story.

By Jove! Speaking of those who ought to be at a
certain distance in order to treat their subject properly
has led me away from my own. To come back to Fontenoy: I am finally inclined to believe that *"Messieurs les
Anglais,* fire first"* is the historic form of the very French
"Après vous."

No, one cannot consider people who do not eat with
their elbows kept close to their sides, who gesticulate as
they talk, talk while they are eating, and often talk
about what they are eating, who, far from waiting until
the ladies have left the room, begin with the soup
course telling the most improper stories in their presence,
who think they are absolutely obliged to flirt with your

wife, who feel it would be rude to arrive at 8:30 when
they are invited for 8:30, who kiss in public even if they
happen to be men, who never seem to finish buttoning
themselves up in the street and communicate with the
trees when they go to the country, who never think of
seating a lady at the dinner table, who dare to call a
man a murderer because he has killed four people when
the police have not proved it, who talk to people they
do not know, especially in trains, without being forced
to do so by some accident, who do not know how to
brew proper tea, do not understand the first thing about
cricket, try to force their way into the middle of waiting
lines, who consider it a laudable feat to drive their car
the wrong way down a one-way street, who go out without an umbrella merely because it is not raining, who in
their newspapers call one of our young lords a homo-
sexual when it would be so simple just to write that he
accosted young men, who try to pass through the auto-
matic doors on the Metro while they are closing, who
speak of a man's mistress before mentioning his wife,
who use toothpicks at the table, which would not be noticed if they did not feel obliged to spread their left

hands fanwise over their mouths, who are much more ready to hang up the receiver than to apologize when they get a wrong number on the telephone, who wear their best clothes on Sundays (except, perhaps, for a few I know in Lyon or Bordeaux who have a venerable Britannico-Aquitaine background)—no, as I say, one cannot consider these people civilized or even polite, at least not in the English (i.e., correct) sense of the term.

For a final example, take their attitude toward women. When an Englishman passes a pretty woman in the street, he sees her without looking at her, never turns around, and retains a "correct" image of her in his mind. Usually when a Frenchman passes a pretty woman in the street, he first looks at her legs to see if she is really all she seemed at first glance; then he turns around to have a better view, and eventually realizes he is going in the same direction she is.

Polite? The French? Gallant, rather! Damned gallant!!

One must do them this justice: they are the champions of: "After you." "No, after you."

The French, who, as we have seen, devote a considerable part of their day to handshaking, also spend an appreciable amount of time asking one another into one another's homes. As some are begging others to enter, the others declare they would not want to impose. The first then insist. Since the days of Charlemagne, the French have spent (roughly) three and a half centuries on one another's doorsteps. Astonishing that we ever find any of them in their homes at all!

I have always found the attraction doorsteps hold for Frenchmen rather strange. Once they reach this spot, they have a way of saying good-by without actually going which you find nowhere in the Commonwealth, nor perhaps in any other part of the world. At the very moment when, after two hours' talk, they say they must be leaving, precisely then do they find the most urgent things to say. The same thing is true for women on the telephone: the word "good-by" is a signal for the conversation to be continued.

I was particularly struck by this attitude when on my return to France after a long absence on a mission in Mesopotamia I thought I must be suffering from a hal-

The behavior of a French pedestrian . . .

. . . and of an English equestrian

(PSYCHODRAWING BY PROFESSOR WALTER GOETZ)

lucination. There was my old friend M. Taupin in exactly the same position in which I had left him six months earlier: on his doorstep still saying good-by to M. Charnelet. My experience in the desert had accustomed me to mirages: I could not believe my eyes. Discreetly I drew near. I saw M. Taupin take a few steps back, raise his arms in the air, then advance threateningly upon M. Charnelet, seize him by his coat lapels, and proceed to shake him backwards and forwards. It was clear—at least, to an Englishman—that they were on the point of coming to blows. My English major's heart stood still; I was preparing to separate them when I heard them burst out laughing. At that moment they noticed me.

"Good Heavens," cried M. Taupin, "here's our Major Thompson come back! What a surprise!"

I knew then that my eyes had not deceived me. At once M. Taupin asked me in, and M. Charnelet, after saying good-by once more, on thinking it over, soon joined us for a chat.

Chapter 6

THE CASE OF COUNT RENAUD DE LA CHASSELIÈRE

The English have two possessions of outstanding value: their tweeds and their silences. The soft, firm texture of the first is equaled only by the noble density of the second. I am prepared to offer ten bottles of Scotch to any explorer who discovers anywhere in the world a silence comparable to that produced by a dozen gentlemen in a St. James's Street club immersed in their somnolent perusal of *The Times.*

The French, who willingly affirm that silence is golden, should therefore admit sportingly that England is a rich country. It is, above all, in conversation that our silences are so remarkable. That is why aliens[1] find so much difficulty in understanding us.

How in the devil do the English manage to keep silent and talk at the same time?

By their "and—er."

"And—er," the loom on which silent conversation is woven, is one of the oldest and most respected of British traditions. From time to time an Englishman may converse in a drawing-room. It may even happen—for almost anything can happen—that you meet a loquacious Englishman. In that case, he pauses, realizes that no one is answering him except by grunts, and answers himself. A foreigner meeting this kind of person who cuts his monologues in two might think he was hearing a dialogue. But the well-bred Englishman—that is to say, an Englishman—very soon stops talking. He makes a short pause, then from the depths of his throat emerges a cavernous "and—er."

wwwwwwwwww

[1] Foreigners, but the term "foreigners" gives little idea of the curious sensation of uneasiness and the real inferiority complex that this word "alien" confers upon its recipient. "So you're not a British subject, you're an *alien*—" and at once the visitor feels uncomfortable, set apart, suffering perhaps from some contagious disease.

With other races the "er" implies that something is to follow. Not so with the English. Something may follow. Generally it doesn't. What happens to whatever *might* have followed nobody knows. One thing is certain —it very rarely appears. This is the very height of reserve and discretion.

Does this mean that the English do not talk? No. Certainly they talk, but how differently from the French! In France, where one asserts one's brilliance by the spoken word, the man who is silent is committing social suicide. In England, where the whole art of conversation consists precisely in knowing how to be silent, a man shows his brilliance by his dull side.

Take, for example, the weather.

The French may be masters of conversation, but they are mere babes when it comes to the weather. This is a specialty in which the English are unrivaled. In justice to the French it must be said that they do not even attempt to compete with their British neighbors in this field. In France, to talk about rain or fine weather amounts to a confession that one is incapable of talking about anything else. In England it is a sacred duty and the sign of proper upbringing. To be a really good Englishman you must be able to talk about the weather—the weather we have got now, the weather we have had, the weather we may possibly have. The word "weather" recurs more than any other in conversation, a key word, a commanding word: weather—rainy weather, cloudy weather, dreadful weather, stormy weather, incredible weather!

Probably in the beginning of things weather was created partly to allow the English to talk about it. Really, there is no other country in the world where it is talked about so much. Perhaps that is why it is so bad there. The impressive expenditure of meteorological vocabulary every day in England must upset the atmosphere.

That is not the only difference between a Frenchman and Englishman in conversation. Far from it.

In France people exaggerate the smallest incident. In England they minimize the greatest catastrophe. If a Frenchman arrives at dinner an hour late because he has mistaken the day, he will talk all evening about his extraordinary adventure. If an Englishman arrives a few minutes late because the roof of his house fell in, he will say that he was delayed by a *slight disturbance.*[2]

In England, we never allow truth to enter naked into our drawing-rooms. In France, the franker one is, the better. In England, we take care not to allude in public to people's private lives—no personal remarks. In France, on the contrary, people wallow in voracious intimacy with their neighbors.

I know that we are not exactly soft. I know that our so-called "historical cruelty" has led us to do some very nasty things, especially in 16° South latitude.[3] I know, too, that in England, as elsewhere, people gossip, and that, in general, two women do not get on well together unless they are on the back of a third.

But I know of nothing more cruel (if we except the

[2] This is one of the many forms of understatement so dear to the British heart. After a night of one of the most frightful bombings of the war, Major Thompson said to me next morning, with a smile: "We had a bit of a picnic last night."

[3] Was the Major alluding to St. Helena or to the Boers or the Fiji Islands, all of which fall into that latitude? It was impossible to persuade him to be more precise.

customs of certain Continental nations still in a state of barbarism) than a French salon.

The only proof I will bring forward is the curious story of Count Renaud de la Chasselière.

I had been asked to dinner by the Pochets. There were about a dozen guests, who, at first, were talking of one thing and another—that is, of everything. With the soup we discussed the cinema, then we had some existentialist trout, an E.D.C. chicken, Four Great Powers with the salad, and flying saucers with the *entremets*. With the French, conversation moves at breathtaking speed. They make you leap from the hydrogen bomb to the Roland Petit ballet, from the Kremlin to the Patinos case, and all with such ease that an ex-major in the Indian Army finds it more difficult to follow them than to stalk a tiger in the Bengali jungle. And, Gad, what marvelous shots! Even with his Winchester .375 Magnum, my friend Basil Cranworth,[4] who was considered one of the finest shots in Assam, could not have obtained such

wwwwwwwwwww

[4] V.C., C.S.I., O.B.E., ex-officer in the 6oth Burma Rifles.

results. Once caught in their fire, there is no escape.

As it happened, the siege of Count Renaud de la Chasselière began in the drawing-room at about 22 hours 30. At that moment the Count, though absent, was, as far as I know, still whole. All I knew about him was that he occupied an important post at the Quai d'Orsay and had conducted himself brilliantly during the war.

At 22:34 M. Pochet opened fire with: "You know, he's no more a count than I am!" That blew off his coronet.

At 22:40 he could no longer be called de la Chasselière; it appeared that he had taken the name—and forgotten to give it back—from a place near his estate in Sologne. His name was simply Renaud.

"And not even with a *-d*," added a member of the artillery. "With an *-lt!*"

"Like those little Renault cars?" asked someone.

"Exactly!"

"Well!" said the authentic Baron de Leaumes with a frown.

The Count was already rather badly shot up when at 22:50 a well-informed gentleman revealed that he

The drawing (and quartering) room

(AFTER REMBRANDT)

had got into the Quai d'Orsay only by a fluke and had never passed the Foreign Office exams.

At 22:55 a lady scored a bull by whispering that the Countess "had everything it takes to be utterly commonplace."

This sly barrage was followed up at once by the supporting fire of one of the guests who hitherto had not fired a shot. He now caught the enemy in the rear, so to speak, by revealing that for a father of four children, his morals—well, to speak frankly—!

I do not know what impelled me then—perhaps that old English mania for giving a fair chance to the man who is downed in battle. Not knowing that I was to strike him with it, I threw the count a lifebuoy:

"But what about the war? Didn't he do very well in the war?"

"As well as everybody else did—so what?"

The English would never have forgiven this clumsy initiative to give the conversation another turn, and I could only be sorry that I had once again betrayed my mother tongue, silence.

At 23 hours precisely, the Count Renaud de la Chasselière fell—annihilated.

A sad story, no doubt.

Not so sad, however, if one reflects that at the same moment, only a mile away, Count Renaud de la Chasselière with other eminent practitioners, in a similar drawing (and quartering) room, amputated the titles of the Baron de Leaumes, the Pochets, and several others, so that at midnight there was nothing left of them.

Chapter 7

THE LAWS OF HOSPITALITY
AND GASTRONOMY

The French may be regarded as the most hospitable people in the world so long as you do not want to enter their homes.

Many foreigners who intend to spend some time in France dream of living with a French family. After several unsuccessful attempts I have discovered that the best way to manage it—short of becoming a governess, which, it must be admitted, is somewhat difficult for a British major, even if he wears kilts—is to establish oneself on the spot, find a Frenchwoman who will have you, and start your own family. That is what I did.

When you have met an Englishman, unless you shock him by an excess of intelligence or curiosity, at the end of an hour's acquaintance he will ask you to spend the week-end in his cottage. Five years later you will discover that you do not really know whether he likes women, men, or postage stamps.

At the end of an hour, sometimes sooner, a Frenchman will have told you how and why he is occasionally led to leave his wife, though he assures you by the way that she is "really very nice—an angel—but, of course, you know how it is—" (How on earth *should* I know?) Ten years afterwards you will realize that you have never spent a night under his roof.

When I went to Lyon for the first time, M. Taupin warned me: "Now, remember! Lyon society is very exclusive—but be patient. When they get to know you, you'll be received everywhere."

He explained that this was a particular trait of Lyon society. Yet I received exactly the same advice (and every time with an insistence on the purely local character of the attitude) at Bordeaux, Lille, Marseille, and even at Mazamet. *Most important,* Mazamet. You

"Once they've taken you in, you'll be one of the family"

may know Paris, Roubaix, Toulouse, and Carcassonne: you will not know France if you do not know Brisbane-sur-Arnette—I mean Mazamet, capital of the sheep-and-woolen-stocking country. There, as elsewhere, I was told before entering fine private houses with austere façades:

"Once they've taken you in, you'll see, you'll be one of the family!"

This is another of the vicious circles in which France is so rich: to be received you must be known, and to be known you must be received. The difficult thing about closed societies is entering them in the first place. It is no good "to stay shut outside," as they say in Limoges when they have forgotten their latch-key.[1]

Just how long must this period of observation—I was going to say incubation—last? Impossible to say exactly. Some say six months or a year. That is an optimistic estimate. It can last ten, twenty years. The best thing is to prepare for the second generation, which will

---

[1] Cf. the expression "stop coming in," which the Limousins use for someone who seems to be getting congealed on the doorstep (*Major's note*).

start being received, then receive in its turn, and finally become very exclusive.

I must admit that there is a great difference between Paris and the provinces of France.

In the provinces you are at once told: "They're very exclusive." You are told about the Central European businessman who for seven years laid siege to Bordeaux without ever effecting a breach, or about the family from Oran which waited half a century before doors were opened to it (and which, of course, in its turn became very exclusive). In the end, after all, you are received.

In Paris you are not received at all: you are taken out. The arrival of the Nicholsons or the Martinezes has a rather curious effect upon their Parisian friends. I happened to be at the Daninoses' one day when the telephone announced the imminent arrival—I believe they spoke of the landing—of the Svenssons, whom they had stayed with for a fortnight in Stockholm. The announcement of a major catastrophe could not have caused greater dismay.

"We'll have to take them everywhere!" I heard.

Faced with the prospect of such a trial, my hosts seemed terribly tempted not to take them anywhere at all. The "dinner at home with us" having been put off to a later date, the Svenssons were invited "to have a drink" at a café in the Champs-Élysées, and in the end, after some days of gaining time, taken to one of those sanctuaries of Art and Pleasure into which Parisians rarely venture unless accompanied by foreign mentors.

I must say, in defense of the French in general and the Daninoses in particular, that the Svenssons' appetite is colossal. I do not mean for meals (though many foreigners who eat practically nothing at home simply gorge themselves when with the French), but for buildings— Gunnar Svensson is a redoubtable devourer of stone buildings. I had always been inclined to believe that the Swedish stomach was modeled on the same pattern as any other. Not so. He swallowed the Sacré Cœur like an hors d'œuvre.

"Now," said Svensson, "vee must see Catacombs."

If the Catacombs had been in Florence, M. Daninos would doubtless have already visited them three times. But as he has lived in Paris for the last forty years, he had not yet got around to visiting them. He only remembered that one day, when he was seven years old, his father said: "If you're a good boy, I'll take you to the Catacombs on Sunday." He could not have been good, because he never went.

My hosts tried to dissuade Gunnar. "Wouldn't you rather go and have a drink in the Place du Tertre?"

Foreigners sometimes have fixed ideas. Gunnar wanted Catacombs. Just try confusing a Swede some day!

"That's easy," said his host. "I'll take you there." A Frenchman is most annoyed when he has to confess that he is unacquainted with the Catacombs. But not even to know where to look for them is worse. On the pretext of buying some cigarettes, my friend and collaborator went off to tackle a policeman: "What's the best way to the Catacombs?" The policeman hesitated, then took out his pocket guidebook. They might have clasped hands—a rare moment of understanding between two Frenchmen!

As for hospitality as such, I believe it is easier for an American to gain admittance to the drawing-rooms of

Buckingham Palace than to lunch with the Taupins. On arrival he is told: "You really must come to lunch with us. Yes, yes, indeed you must!" Weeks pass. Something unforeseen happens: the children are ill, the cook has given notice. The Parisian ends by taking the foreigner, so avid for local color, to an American grill where the menu is not even printed in French, as it would be in the U.S.A.

I exaggerate, no doubt. If you stay more than six months in France, you are, I admit, at last invited by certain families. Then you are warned: "You'll have to take pot luck." Pot luck, an emaciated affair in England, assumes in France the most ample proportions. It explains the whole mystery: when you take pot luck with the French and see what trouble they have taken, you realize why this improvisation, like the speech of a Member of Parliament, must be prepared long beforehand. No English hostess could achieve such results without months of work. The whole question is, then, whether it is better to be invited at once by the English or to wait six months to be invited by the French. For my part, I incline to the French way. Good Lord, the meal is so splendid one does not mind having waited!

It is not enough that their pot luck is Pantagruelian: they start your mouth watering with dishes that do not appear on the table. For example, when, freed from the constraint of British tact, I venture to talk about what I am eating and praise the leg of lamb *à l'anglaise*, M. Taupin exclaims:

"Ah, if only you'd been here three weeks ago we'd have given you a pheasant—oh, what a pheasant!"

"Actually a hen pheasant—you remember, Tounet? [2] It was plump—melted in your mouth—and, mind you, not too high, just right. Ah, Major—!"

The French have the true gourmand's way of evoking memories of good fare which enables them to enjoy word banquets between meals. It is an incomparable pleasure for a foreigner to be their contemplative guest. On their lips the mere name of Pommard or Château Margaux emerges so rich, so velvety—already *chambré* —that they reveal to you all the fluid treasures of Burgundy and all the secrets of the Bordeaux vine.

[2] Short for Gaston, pet name used by Mme Taupin.

In this instance, the pheasant—I apologize, the hen pheasant—was there diffusing over the table the smell of game. Yet it was really a leg of lamb—succulent, I must say. But with these people you never know exactly where you are.

When a country possesses so many good things, each may be enjoyed many times over. Only with a native's memory can one have such a gastronomical calendar on the top of his tongue. I have not and doubtless never shall. I realized that on my first visit to this country. When I arrived at Castelnaudary, old Piquemolles said: "You're a bit late for my little fresh livers. But I can make you a nice little *cassoulet* of preserved goose that will give you something to write home about. You don't eat it, you suck it."

"Oh, yes, Mr. Piquemolles—a nice little *cassoulet*."

Then when I went on to the Pyrenees, "It's a bit early for wood pigeon, Major," said M. Cabrioules. "What would you say to a nice little haunch of chamois?"

"Oh, yes, Mr. Cabrioules—a little haunch of chamois."

Everywhere I went I was given good things to eat

France: a tourist's paradise

only to be made to regret that I had not been given better. Marvelous country! So different from my own, where, because all the year round we eat the same things cooked in the same way, regret, like hope, is out of place.

Chapter 8

MARTINE AND URSULA

I have experienced once in my life an upheaval comparable to the crumbling of the Pillars of Hercules. It was when Martine said:

"I love those little silver threads in your mustache."

We were walking along by the Seine on one of those sunny March mornings when the pastel blue sky of the Île de France behaves like a coy springtime beginning its flirtation with the gray stonework of the French Institute. I felt my world rocking; the corset of Victorian convention was bursting apart: I was definitely falling into the sentimental universe of the Latins. No longer was I "the honorable Major Thompson, C.S.I., D.S.O., O.B.E." I was about to become the husband of Martine Noulet—"you know, that incredible Englishman with the white mustache. . . ."

Across the Channel one does not speak to a person about details so personal as his mustache or the mole on his cheek. (Indeed, there are so many things that are not done in England that the unsuspecting visitor might well believe that love-making was one of them.) I had to go to France to learn—in any detail—my own geography. I mean my own personal atlas, those capes and bays and valleys which interested Ursula so little and of which Martine made such a tender and accurate survey. Ursula would never have spoken to me in such topographical language. I still remember the expressions she used when I could not bring myself to speak at all:

"The two of us—after all— What about it?"

It is after frantic declarations of this kind that English couples marry.

That is how I came to marry Ursula.

Actually, it wasn't so much love that united us as a mutual passion for horses.

The first time I glimpsed Ursula (there are some women who should only be glimpsed) she was riding Lazy Lassie in the Dublin Horse Show. She had a way of riding at breakneck speed over this track—its fixed obstacles were among the stiffest in the world—and of turning around in the space of a handkerchief which attracted the most uninitiated eye. The consummate skill with which she "negotiated the oxer" [1] was even more telling. With her hunting bowler, her tight-fitting black coat, white buckskin breeches, and top boots, she was truly a brave sight. The presentation of the Gold Cup gave me the opportunity to congratulate her. She talked of India and of pig-sticking.[2] We soon had to part, but an understanding had been created, and a few weeks later, when fox-hunting had begun and I met her again at the Quorn hunt, we were naturally drawn toward each other. It was the end of a gorgeous autumn, and the countryside and woods of Leicestershire were still re-

[1] To "negotiate the oxer" or to "negotiate the hills": expressions favored by English sportsmen. Certain French reporters are beginning to use the term, though Napoleon would have seen therein yet another mark of "a nation of shopkeepers" (*Major's note*).

[2] Pig-sticking: a most favored sport with the English in India.

splendent in reds and golds. Whether it was due to the beauties of nature or to our horsy memories, I cannot say; in any case, we tarried and lost sight of the hunt.

As we crossed the little village of Ratcliffe we pulled up at the Marlborough Arms for a comforting whisky or two. Then we made our way over fields and hills, gaily jumping hedges and fences and streams. We must have been about ten miles from Brookby when, to give our horses a breather and ourselves a rest, we dismounted under the trees on the banks of the River Wreak. For an instant the silence of the countryside was broken by the sound of a furious gallop. A hundred yards away we saw a straggling horseman, who looked like the young Earl of Hertford, riding like a whirlwind over the little stone bridge. A few seconds later we heard the distant call of the huntsman and the baying of the hounds. The hunt was a long way off.

That day we were certainly not good sportsmen. Perhaps it had become clear to us both that there were other obstacles besides those of Dublin and Leicestershire we could tackle together. We sat down beside the water. I could not describe exactly what happened next;

Ursula was a (brave) sight

it was so sudden and extraordinary. The embrace sheltered by the noble oaks on Lord Cambleforth's estate was a compound of love, the hunt, and whisky, in equal parts.

Why do so many women change, the moment you marry them? I was destined never to recapture the passionate moment that decided my fate. Everything changed from the minute I saw Ursula in a dressing-gown. I had been attracted by her "presence," the way she moved, her distinction—all those qualities which were inseparable from the Horse Show, and which attenuated her features: her long nose, large ears, and rather prominent jaw. After a time, stable boys who live day and night with horses, by some mysterious mimetic process, get to look like horses. So in Ursula was there something of the horse. When she was in riding-habit the horse face did not matter. When we were alone together, it was quite different. The amazon vanished; only the mare remained.

At first I tried to make Ursula wear as often as possible the outfit in which I admired her. But I could not expect her to sleep in her bowler. No doubt my insistence seemed strange to her. From the day we went into our Hampshire home Ursula gave up riding. There was a reason for that, but I discovered it only later. Her way of laughing and joking without restraint was quite changed. Evidently the fact that she now had to look after a house and manage servants made her more serious and formal. She was no longer a club friend, a comrade in competitions. She was mistress of a house and much less ready to laugh at a joke than to discover traces of dust everywhere—especially on my feet.

"Mind your feet when you come in, dear. . . . Wipe your feet. . . . You've been in here with your feet again, Thompson!"

Perhaps somewhere there exists a race of men who manage to go about without their feet. It is beyond my powers. In fact, all our trouble began with our feet. By always talking to me about feet, Ursula finally forced me to look at hers. In well-made shoes most feet are passable. In a slipper Ursula's foot assumed gigantic proportions—a detail which, I may say, had not struck me at first because everyone said of Ursula: "She's got a good head on her shoulders." (One ought to be suspicious of such compliments.)

How shall I—keeping within the limits of decency—describe my life with Ursula?

Perhaps in just that one word—"decency." This athlete, rough-rider, relentless huntress, suddenly became metamorphosed into a paragon of decency.

"Now, then. . . . Don't be sloppy, dear. Stop that nonsense. . . ." Of course, all Englishwomen are not Ursula, yet explaining Ursula helps to explain England. Freud would have felt at home here; everything can be explained by the word "inhibition." In the roistering days of Henry VIII or George IV, this country was the scene of the most extravagant feasting and maddest orgies. The Victorian era set up a gigantic repression factory whose disciples are still hard at it. Ursula was the descendant of a formidable bastion of the Victorian fortress. In the manor house at Trent where she was born, her grandmother, Lady Plunkwell, rigidly practiced Wesleyan principles: you must never mention the word "legs" (you must say "extremities" or "lower limbs"), and piano legs are to be swathed in muslin.[3]

When Ursula was eleven she was sent to Meltenham School in Warwickshire, a school governed by the dual laws of monastic puritanism and athleticism. When she left, six years later, she may not have known how a boy was made, but she herself had become one.

Once again, I am anxious to guard against generalities, but I sincerely believe that if Englishmen could only have discovered some means of bringing children into the world without having anything to do with women, they would be the happiest people on earth. The first care in British education is to separate the two sexes as if they were never to meet again (they do not in fact meet often). While the girls are sent to institutions where their legs are encased in black stockings, and where they learn to blush for the evil sins of the flesh and even blush at the flesh itself (at Meltenham the rule stigmatizing nudity forced the pupils to take their baths wearing a cotton nightdress), the boys are

[3] Today this practice is very rarely observed: but in England it is still always safer to avoid mentioning anything that lies between the chin and the knees.

sent off to schools where they learn to their amazement that, besides cricket and the Colonial Office, they will from time to time have to think about women.

It is not right to say that in England nothing is planned for women. It is normal that a small boy's principal aim in life should be to become a man, but in the United Kingdom it is also the aim of every little girl. The mistresses at Meltenham exhorted their charges to "Run like boys, girls, run"—which was their way of suggesting: "That will keep you from thinking about them." And Ursula ran like a boy, and the exercise purged her of the passions and evil thoughts she might otherwise have entertained. At a time when Martine and her friends were becoming romantic and reading *"On ne badine pas avec l'amour,"* Ursula and her comrades were performing marvels at lacrosse and singing: "I'm so glad . . . I'm not pretty."

Years may pass, worlds be overturned by wars, governments rise and fall, but the Meltenham rule leaves its indelible imprint upon the soul. The woman I married bore the Meltenham mark even in the way she slept. Some time after she had entered the school, a mistress going the rounds of the icy dormitories one winter's night discovered Ursula sleeping rolled up in a ball under the sheets.

"My child," she said, "is that a decent position to sleep in? Just suppose you were to die in the night, would that be the proper way to meet your Maker?"

From that night on Ursula slept according to rule: on her back, with her feet out in the cold and her hands crossed upon her breast. I admit that it is a very suitable attitude for kings and queens immobilized in stone who slumber in Westminster Abbey under the eyes of the passing generations. But as for spending the night with a normally constituted man, there are more convenient attitudes. I should be suppressing the truth if I omitted to say that on my suggestion Ursula did try to cultivate a more conjugal slumber and go to sleep in my arms. But, every time, the Meltenham rule returned at night, haunting her subconscious. And if I happened to wake, I found myself alongside a statue.

I know. . . . Not all Englishwomen sleep like that. Not every daughter of Albion has large feet and prominent jaws. There are ravishing Englishwomen, and when

they are pretty they make up for all those who are not.
There are volcanic Englishwomen whose fire and spar-
kle illuminate all Great Britain and her dominions. Ursula was doubtless a "case." In Ursula's case, love was
simply not interesting. The storm which broke on the
banks of the Wreak had passed forever. Shy girls sometimes have overwhelming attacks of boldness and then
withdraw forever into their true characters.

Sport in general, and competitive sport in particular,
never predisposed anyone to the languors of love. The
Meltenham mistresses knew that, and the intensive practice of lacrosse tended to sweat out harmful ideas. When
Ursula grew up, riding took the place of lacrosse. There
again she was unlike those rare devotees of horseman-
ship whose activity in no way damps their ardor; the
horse broke Ursula. I might perhaps have hoped at the
beginning, when I saw her abandon her favorite sport,
that with tranquillity would come the reawakening of
her instincts. I was wrong: Meltenham prevailed. I soon
realized the meaning of the interruption and what was
expected of me. If she had for the moment given up riding, it was not for the sake of a husband, it was for Eng-

land and the human race. Meltenham and her mother had prepared her for marriage in an entirely Victorian spirit. The day before she left home, Lady Plunkwell had delivered her final advice:

"I know, my dear, it's disgusting. But do as I did with Edward: just close your eyes and think of England!"

Like her mother and her mother's mother before her, Ursula closed her eyes. She thought of the future of England. And the future of England is certainly something sacred which her subjects are right in standing up for; but somehow, to the minute extent to which it depended upon my small contribution, this future was not assured. Doubtless it was decreed that the future of Great Britain would be better assured by me in France. . . .

As soon as Ursula realized that Heaven was not going to grant us its favors, she went back into training. Indeed, she took it up again with a spirit that bordered on frenzy. Rising at six, she spent the whole day with horses, stable boys, the oxer, the Irish hurdle, and on the special track I had been foolish enough to have made for her as a wedding present. In the evening, tired out, she supervised the grooming and inspected the harness. When she came in she would take off her boots, throw herself onto a sofa or her bed, and sink into sleep. Or else she would take up her embroidery.

She did not refuse to do what she believed to be her duty. But at the decisive moment she always gave me a guilt complex—the feeling of guilt a schoolboy has when he is caught reading the Medical Dictionary.

"You should be ashamed of yourself! . . . Put the light out. . . . Naughty boy!"

Was there somewhere under this ice floe a fire smoldering? I am cautious about women in general, and about Englishwomen in particular. Under a mask of coldness the most bizarre and inadmissible yearnings may be positively swarming. One Sunday I found Ursula reading *News of the World* and enjoying the carefully prepared report of one of those conjugal dramas which are the Sunday delight of even the most stolid English homes. It was the story of an honest Liverpool tradesman who was seeking his freedom after ten years of slavery, during which his wife forced him to play horse and trotted him around the room with a whip. Ursula burst into derisive laughter:

"That would suit you perfectly!"

I do not know if it would have suited me, but the idea of a major in the Indian Army harnessed like a pony and shaking the bells of his harness made a somewhat startling picture. I began to wonder whether Ursula's indifference was only apparent, and whether that habit of going on with her damned embroidery right up to the psychological moment was not, after all, the very essence of perversion.

Decades of light years lay between me and Martine's planet, the emotional universe of the French. May I now pass on from the particular to the general and, after carefully emphasizing that England is not exclusively peopled with Ursulas, note down what I consider an essential difference between the two countries? The English observe rites for making tea, and have habits in making love. The French devote to love the care we bring to making tea. In general, love with us is a kind of rapid sleight of hand, not to be discussed before nor afterward. For the French it is a full-length, most carefully produced play, arranged with a prologue and intermezzos, and much discussed before, during, and after. The French are the gastronomes of love, the English its performers.

Far from asking, like Martine: "Was it nice? Are you pleased? Very, very pleased?" Ursula would have been more likely to inquire whether I felt better. In point of fact, she did not ask me anything. This behavior, moreover, is not peculiar to Ursula, far from it. Even when they happen to be fond of love, the English do not talk about it. They leave that to their playwrights or newspapers.[4] Probably the most beautiful love-duets in any tongue were written by Shakespeare. But his is not the language the English use for ordinary purposes. And if

wwwwwwwwwwww

[4] Which have their own way of speaking of it. The *New Statesman and Nation* of March 27, 1954, quotes this sentence from an article in *News of the World:* "Love is a word we have got to be very careful about. In certain connections it has a sexual significance."

they happen to talk of love, they find it necessary to soften the language of Beowulf with imported terms like *"tête-à-tête," "c'est l'amour,"* or *"rendezvous."* [5]

As for the press, we have seen that it does not hesitate to report conjugal dramas or to embroider endlessly a princely idyl. Let a Royal Princess change her cavalier or fail to smile before setting out for Southern Rhodesia and all the large-circulation newspapers set about finding reasons for her depression. (*"Why is the Princess so sad?"*) And then my dear England, my strict, softhearted England, so tightly laced in the corset of her traditions, my England which feels herself a little bit a part of the Royal Family, becomes passionately anxious to discover whose face is floating through the Princess's imagination as she inspects the dances of the feathered warriors of Bechuanaland. Very respectfully, but with an insistence that would be out of place in a less polite country, reporters scrutinize the sad countenance, trying to find out what is behind it. . . .

[5] It is interesting to note that an up-to-date French girl who finds *"Je vous aime"* old-fashioned will cheerfully write: "I love you."

. . .

I have always tried to measure as carefully and accurately as possible the distance that separates Frenchmen from Englishmen. I wish I could do this with their sentimental affairs, but my measuring-instruments fall from my hands. The barrier is not a moat, it is an abyss.

In France a pretty woman (every woman manages to be pretty in this country, even those who are not) would be shocked if a man did not pay some attention to her in a drawing-room, or failed to notice her new frock. Only in a husband might she possibly conceive of such an attitude, while publicly deploring that he no longer sees her with a lover's eyes.

In England a pretty woman finds it "most shocking" if a man kisses her hand, and very bad form if he compliments her on her complexion—unless, of course, he is her husband, and then he would not think of doing such a thing.

Martine expects a dress to be elegant. Ursula and her friends would want *something to be comfortable in.*[6]

[6] I must confess that in dress Englishwomen have made marked progress in the last few years. But acquired habits stick (*Major's note*).

First marriage
St. Marks
Audley Street
(1929)

Second marriage
Mairie of the
XVIth Arrondissement
(1932)

Out of doors the Parisian wearing a new spring tailored suit is secretly delighted to see the glint it produces in a man's eye. So would an Englishwoman be, of course, but such a spark is hard to imagine in a land where a man's glance, probably because of the surrounding dampness, seems to be incombustible. Frenchmen run after women; Englishmen merely run across them.

In France women do all they can to be noticed, but express great surprise if a man they do not know does notice them enough to mention the fact. A *femme du monde*[7] is scandalized if she is accosted, but bitterly disappointed if she is not. "I'm never followed now," she will say one day, thereby acknowledging her age and her disillusionment.

An Englishwoman can be perfectly confident on this matter: nobody will accost her. If such an extraordinary thing should happen, if some suspicious-looking foreigner thought of following her, the dependable bobby

[7] In France a *femme du monde* is a woman who does not belong to anybody (not even to her husband), probably in contradistinction to the *demi-mondaines,* who belong to everybody.

would soon restore things to their all too dependable order. The policemen of the two countries in this, as in other things, are very different. Martine once told me that when she was very young, but not too young to be followed, she rushed up to a policeman and said: "Oh, policeman, that man is following me!" "I am sorry that my duties prevent me from doing the same, mademoiselle!" said he, calmly continuing to direct the traffic. These are only minor differences.[8]

The real antagonism lies elsewhere. Often, when a Frenchman is being discussed, you learn a little about the man himself, a great deal about his mistress, and nothing at all about his wife. When an Englishman is being discussed, you are told a great deal about him, but very little is said about his wife, and nothing at all about his mistress. I am inclined to believe that a Frenchman without a mistress is like an Englishman without a club, but— By Jove! Far be it from me to generalize.

[8] It should be noted that if the methods of the police in Paris and London vary, their effect on "followers" is the same; the man makes off.

·   ·   ·

One thing is clear: the predilection of Frenchmen for boudoir adventure and the care they take in bringing up their children in the respect of family traditions combine to make France, of all countries in the world, the one in which it is simplest to live a complicated life and most complicated to live a simple life. With us English, complications are rarer and less visible. Being without children lessens hesitations about divorce. On the other hand, we hesitate longer before committing a "crime of passion," which under French law sometimes appears to be regarded as a virtuous accomplishment.

An Englishman is governed by the single law "it isn't cricket" even in his sentimental misadventurers: he has to know how to part with his wife as gracefully as if he were losing a game. If he should unfortunately show himself to be a bad loser and kill his rival, he is soon told that this is one of the things that is not done. He need not count on any leniency in court. On the other side of the Channel he would doubtless have been congratulated by the jury. At home he receives a polite letter, beginning "Dear Sir" and ending "Yours faithfully," which tells him that unfortunately he will have to be hanged.

In France, where women have no legal rights, everything is done for women and by women. "Rue de la Paix," "magistracy," "irony," "revolution," "gallantry," "Republic": these are all words that in French are feminine—and rightly.

In England, where legally women have every juridic right, nothing is suited to women. Not even men. Ships are feminine, but, apart from that, the masculine prevails: the greatest compliment one can pay a woman is to say that she is a good sport.

That is just what they said about Ursula. We have seen how Meltenham had masculinized her. In England everything works hand in hand with this vast conspiracy against women: the intensive practice of sports during adolescence deprives the female of her tender feelings, the clubs take away her husband, schools take away her children, ready-made clothes obscure her charms until the charms themselves begin to fade.

But the age of defeat is her moment of victory. At a time when a Frenchwoman fades into a blur of grays and beiges, the Englishwoman, freed from all constraint, gaily takes her revenge on men. School uniform had suppressed her springtime, so she lives it gloriously later in life, wearing a flower garden on her head, and gloriously attired in baby-blue or salmon-pink dresses. Then, having proclaimed her equal rights, she conducts herself like a man, frequents her club like a man, goes into politics like a man, and, true woman that she is, becomes President of the Society for Lost Finches.[9]

~~~~~~~~~~~~~~~~

[9] It may seem strange to bring in animals when we are talking of women and love. But England is far less the land of "I love you" than the land of "love me, love my dog."

The French eat horses and all kinds of other animals, but never miss a chance of calling one another "my little cat" or "my little sugar hen."

The English, on the other hand, who are far more reserved about this form of address, who approve of corporal punishment for their children, let themselves go in a welter of tender feelings for ponies or dogs. If a watchman at the Tower happens to break his leg by stumbling over his pike, no one takes any notice. But if Judy, a fox terrier belonging to one of the yeomen, should fall ill, as happened recently in London, all London is moved to tears by the bulletins the newspapers publish about its health. I do not know if Abbé Pierre would have collected as much money over here as he did in France, but I am certain he would have collected much more if he had been campaigning for a home for stray cats. No beggar in the kingdom will contradict me when I say that a professional blind beggar will double his receipts if he is accompanied by a sad-eyed dog. Should his dog become blind, he can begin to think of retiring (*Major's note*).

.   .   .

That hour was not to strike for Ursula, but a still more noble one was in store for her.

She fell at Bombay in the Viceroy's Cup, when the hurdle had been put up to six feet. She had insisted on riding an Australian stallion reputed to have a hard mouth.

After refusing the oxer, Bahadur Sahib hit the wall with his chest and, far from clearing it, came a fatal cropper.

It was a complete tragedy; while the unconscious Ursula was being borne away to the British Hospital, Bahadur Sahib had to be shot.

These two faithful servants of equestrianism now repose in Indian soil.

Chapter 9

MY DEAR HEREDITARY

ENEMY . . .

The only source of drama in my life since the death of Ursula is my son. First of all, his Christian name.

I wanted to call him Marmaduke.

Since 1066, calling their eldest son Marmaduke has been a tradition with the Thompsons—who, through their great-great-grandfather, with a little pruning and grafting of his family tree, manage to link up with William the Conqueror. Ursula would not have objected. But my son eventually came to me by my second wife, who is French, and my suggestion made Martine burst out laughing. The name Marmaduke always made her laugh. She says it sounds like marmalade from Dundee. "It's just not a proper name," she says.

To my mind, what is not "proper," at least for an ex-major in the Indian Army, is the name "Doukie," [1] which she made out of it. Good Frenchwoman that she is, she can make a dress out of nothing and a nickname out of anything.

We reached a compromise; the child should be called by the first three letters of both our names, and we added a *c* that he could do what he liked with later on. So he is called Marc. But no power in the world will stop me calling him Marmaduke in secret.

Our discussion on the question of his name was merely the prelude to a tragedy that reached its pitch with the problem of the boy's education.

Good God! Is it really possible that two great nations should have settled in territories as near to each other as France and England just for the sheer pleasure of doing everything in totally different fashions? The French bring children into the world to watch them grow

---

[1] Or, on very good days, "Doukie-doukie" (*Major's note, very embarrassed*).

up. Scarcely have the English seen them born when they send them away to grow up elsewhere. In France children are brought up among grown-ups. In England they become grown-ups among children. The French are sentimental about them; the English toughen them. French parents are somewhat dismayed if their sons show no signs of prodigious intelligence. The English are dismayed if they show any signs at all.[2]

How in such circumstances can we find common ground?

I thought for a while that I had found it in the person of Miss ffyfth.

The boy was to be brought up at first in France with an English governess. At this threat of invasion, all Martine's Breton ancestry sounded the alarm: she hesitated a long time over the intrusion of an auxiliary mother, and an English mercenary at that. I was supported by

[2] I do not mean to say that my honorable compatriots adore idiotic children. But they like children to be children. In France what they like best in a boy is the hint of the man he is going to be. An English father likes to tell you something his son said if it has a comically childish character. Unlike the Frenchman, he will not be proud if the child said something very forward for his age (*Major's note*).

some of her friends who admitted: "Nothing like an Englishwoman for bringing up children," and discouraged
by others who said: "Yes, all very well—but you won't
see anything of him!"

In the end Martine agreed.

It would be inaccurate to write: "Enter Miss ffyfth."
An icy blast from the North Sea was released in the
apartment. With her angular face, her prominent teeth
that resembled tombstones, her long arms, her bony
hands, Miss ffyfth was the picture of rigidity, the incar-
nation of France's hereditary enemy. She was Queen
Elizabeth condemning Mary Queen of Scots to death,
Queen Victoria reclaiming the quagmires of vice with
puritanism, Britannia in a golden helmet seated on a
cask full of slaves. This aboriginal of the first country on
the left above France installed herself as a squatter in
our home. It was not exactly war, but the alert had been
sounded. In the twinkling of an eye the situation became
tense; Florine, the cook, was not going to make porridge
for that dragon, nothing doing (*ça n'y avait rien à
faire*), and Clarissa told her to her face that she could
starve before she got her meals in her room.

I had known Miss ffyfth in India. After doing her first service in some of the most elegant nurseries in the kingdom, Miss ffyfth had been summoned to Kashmir by an Anglomaniac rajah who had decided to entrust to her the training of his son, who was slovenly, indolent, dreamy, and slightly round-shouldered. Miss ffyfth forced this Oriental youngster to wear a rod across his shoulderblades, and trained him with long, hygienic walks ("Breathe deeply—head up—one, two, one, two!") to march like one of Her Majesty's Grenadier Guards, fists swinging violently backwards and forwards. Finally she produced a quite creditable being. When the Englishwoman left Srinagar, the boy was still an Indian, but he was straightened up; he no longer dreamed of comparing a young girl's eyes to hibiscus flowers; his indolence was discarded, and he was ready to admit that Siva had perfected the monsoon in an unsuccessful attempt to test British waterproofs.

At first there were terrible battles over pronunciation. It is difficult for a child who is not completely English to admit that Beauchamp is pronounced "Beecham" and

Leicester "Lest'r." But nobody in the house, from the boy upwards, ever managed to pronounce Miss ffyfth's name correctly. It is a difficult sound to produce, even for the British. Now, Miss ffyfth, who claims that she could give a course of private lessons on her name alone, is very much attached to her patronymic.

There are only a very few old families left today who from medieval times have retained the privilege of beginning their names with a double ration of small *f*'s.[3] Rarer still are those who can add the luxury of a *th*. Only a thousand years' practice can bring off these tricky acrobatics of the tongue without a slip. The French stumble over it and become irritated. Old Florine remarked that she did not need such an expenditure of *f*'s, she

ᴡᴡᴡᴡᴡᴡᴡᴡᴡᴡᴡ

[3] The Major is alluding to those ffoulkes, ffordes, ffrangcon-Davieses, and other old french (no capital) families, who feel singularly ffortified by this impregnable rampart and guard this privilege very jealously. In this respect Miss ffyfth's case is very significant; if she never married, it was from a desire to keep her name, rather than her person, intact. When she was twenty she fell in love with Merthylyd llynfartha. None of the daughters in her family had ever married a man whose name did not begin with *ff* or *Ff*. Her father, after rapidly proving that two *l*'s make no difference, ordered her to stop that nonsense. And so Miss ffyfth remained a virgin (*Major's note*).

would manage just as well with one. (*"Le jour où elle ff—ra le camp, l'Anglaise, elle peut s'en coller quatre des* f . . . *ça ira plus vite!"*)

Martine, who was beginning to lose her self-control, tried to get her own back by letting Miss ffyfth chew on some Broglie, Maupéou, and even some la Trémoille, but the warlike Welsh jaw swallowed the old French nobility whole. The hereditary enemy.

The tension increased. Martine began to realize that some of her friends had been right. After seven o'clock she could not see her son without having a scene. Rules must be respected. Miss ffyfth meant to wash and dress the child, and put him to bed as *she* wished it done, otherwise she refused all responsibility. British rule!

Martine agreed to be patient a little longer, but it soured her disposition. Her mind became strangely retrospective. Hitherto she had never seemed to know who came first, the Normans or the Saxons. Suddenly she strode through the dense forest of English dynasties and hurled at my head the fact that a certain Gourdon was mercilessly flayed alive by Richard Cœur de Lion, as if she had just finished a doctoral thesis on the Plantagenets. At those moments she detested me. I could not understand, she suggested, because I was English.

I do not take offense for so little. When a Frenchman prefaces his words by telling me: "I'll be frank with you, in my family we have always detested the English," I would wager a bottle of Scotch that he will soon assure me: "But really we're very fond of you." For a Frenchman there are always two men in every Englishman, a good one (the Oxford *vs.* Cambridge one) and a bad one (the Fashoda one). Everyone knows that the real, the bona-fide enemy of France is Germany, but, faithful as they are to their time-honored source of nasty feelings, many Frenchmen continue to hand down from father to son the notion of the hereditary British enemy, the most steadfast and cordial antagonist of the Frenchman in time of peace.

To be just, it must be admitted that Miss ffyfth had a rather special way of teaching children history. Sometimes from upstairs I could hear her launching into the Hundred Years' War: "Then King Edward III, led by one of *your* peasants, Gobin Agache, crossed the River

Somme and arrived at a village called Crécy, where he made up his mind to wait and see. . . ."

And the King of England did wait. And he saw the French knights coming. And then began the drama that was to last a hundred years: those mobile English archers armed with wooden bows made of supple ash, their quivers on their hips, always fresh and nimble, and the French knights entangled in their armor, charging in vain under a hail of arrows and never having any luck with weather conditions. *Too bad for the French.* But, added Miss ffyfth, they were *badly led;* they were stifled under their steel helmets, and their methods of warfare were (even then) *old-fashioned.* . . .

Often at the close of a winter day I still think about the Hundred Years' War and about those names—Crécy, Poitiers, Agincourt—which echo in a school in Dorsetshire like shouts of triumph, while twenty leagues away in a Normandy *lycée* they are sounding the knell of French chivalry. Then, as twilight falls and fifty proud little English schoolboys feel the blood of the Black Prince coursing through their veins, sadness fills the hearts of fifty proud little French schoolboys who see John the Good (but Imprudent) led away into captivity in England. Too bad, really. . . .

Meanwhile, Miss ffyfth was striding onward through history. She was sorry for Joan of Arc, who was burned as a witch, but she was careful to point out that the tribunal which condemned her was composed of Frenchmen, and that King Charles VII did nothing to aid the girl (monstrous!). Soon she would get to Napoleon. Without even speaking of Trafalgar or Waterloo; Wellington had already beaten Napoleon at Vimieiro—remember: *Vi-miei-ro.* In the end, the tiresome little man with his funny hat had never been able to realize his dream, which was to go to England. For there was the sea—*la mer*—and, above all, the Br—the Brr—the British navy, dear. . . .

Napoleon had seen England only from afar, for a few minutes on board the *Bellerophon,* which was taking him to St. Helena, but—

"He was not permitted to land."

Not everyone is permitted to land, you see. Napoleon, however Napoleonic he might be, had to obey

Miss ffyfth gives notice

British rule. Marc was probably unconvinced. Miss ffyfth was surprised by his melancholy attitude. She could not understand that a terrible war was raging in the poor child's brain: there was in him a little of Wellington and a little of Napoleon (with a slight prejudice in favor of the man with the funny hat, who was attractive in spite of everything), and in the French half of his mind Grouchy arrived on time at the Battle of Waterloo, while Miss ffyfth had already got Napoleon to St. Helena.

Miss ffyfth's reign lasted two months. It came to an end when the third cook and sixth housemaid had been driven to hysterics by her unreasonable demands and her habit of taking early-morning tea.

One day, realizing that there was something alien and inviolable in the French character (perhaps an anti-Miss complex), she departed with great dignity, having tried to *do her duty to make a real man of Marc.* But the withering look she cast on me when I had been forced to surrender (it was a choice between cooks and her)— oh, Miss ffyfth, that accusing look of yours will haunt me to the grave.

.   .   .

The 1939 war was to consolidate Miss ffyfth's territorial conquests in the tender field of Marc's mind. Our son was on holiday in England when the conflict broke out: we decided he should pursue his studies at a school in Shropshire.

When Marc came back to France he was completely transformed; with his cap, his gray flannel trousers, and his navy-blue waterproof, he seemed definitely British. He had been taught that the earth is a planet occupied by England and a large heap of sand, the Sahara, which was left to the French so that they could amuse themselves by talking of building a railroad. He knew that the most enviable of all possible arrangements that one could ever dream of is incontestably the geographical situation of Great Britain, which shelters it from want and from the tedious promiscuity of foreign invasion. He had admitted that the French, though versatile, agricultural, and witty, had never been able to build really good ships, though they did what they could to become gentlemen by once in their lives buying a hat at Lock's. Brought up under the hard law of masters forever ready to wield the supple cane, and of prefects equally quick to strike, he had recognized that the making of a gentleman begins by accepting a flailing *without grumbling.*

Martine was surprised to find that he seemed to have an instinctive aversion for hand-kissing, was horrified when she discovered that he said "Good night, Mummy" without hugging her.

A week later Marc entered a French boarding-school. There he learned that Joan of Arc had heard real voices (not just "voices"), that a bold seaman named Suffron had had to go right into the Bay of Bengal to find the English ships and give them a lesson, and that in exchange for Canada and India (which had escaped from French hands) England had given only some small change, a few of the lesser Antilles, together with the 5 (five) trading-stations: Pondicherry, Chandernagor, and the three others whose names one never remembers. Good as they were at cricket and golf, the English had nothing really comparable to the "Quarrel between the Ancients and the Moderns." Finally, it was always the French who bore the first brunt in warfare, because the English took so long to get into their uniforms.

Nine months later, exhausted by the word-for-word translation of Cicero's *De Senectute* and the vain pursuit of the square of the hypotenuse, the poor child was nothing but a walking kaleidoscope of information. Wrenched from Trafalgar Square to the Place d'Iéna, and from Waterloo Station to the Gare d'Austerlitz, he discovered that, in the end, men fight not for great causes but for railway lines and crossroads, and that the Latin races in particular spend their lives in the streets named after the 29th of July or 4th of September without knowing exactly what really happened on those days.

In all this incoherence our son seemed to feel quite lost. At all costs, something had to be done to save his tottering reason.

"In any case," said Martine, "there can be no question of sending him back to one of your beastly English schools!"

"Nor will I," I retorted, "let him grow stoop-shouldered in one of your damned French *lycées!*"

In the end, we sent him to Switzerland, that splendid little country which always manages to get the best out of every war, domestic or foreign.

Chapter 10

FRENCH AS SHE IS SPOKEN

I have long tried to discover, without asking point blank, how to speak good French.

In pocket guides one finds: *"Excusez moi. . . . Y a-t-il quelqu'un ici qui parle anglais? . . . Je suis étranger"* written, to make it easier for you: *"Ekskyze-mwa. . . . i jatil kelkoe isi ki parle aglé? . . . ze suiz étrazé."*

One such book has enriched my vocabulary with a host of expressions like: *" 'Garçon, le jacquet' (le zake)* ('Boy, bring the backgammon board')" or *" 'Perçoit-on un droit de péage pour traverser ce pont?'* ('Do I have to pay toll to cross this bridge?')." Its usefulness in case of need I do not deny, but I am ready to part with it at a reasonable price to any true lover of languages.

My difficulty with these handbooks—full of *"tire-boutons* (tirbutô)" and *"harengs bouffis* (bufi)' "[1] so difficult to bring in at the right moment—compelled me for a while to adopt the lazy solution of my countrymen and either not try to speak French at all or else speak it so badly that the French, who pride themselves on "spiking English," come to your aid with some of the "English" they learned at the *lycée: "ze dineur iz raidi."* This ensures you that, in addition to the difficulty of making yourself understood, you will not understand anybody else.

For a British subject there is a third method: not to attack the French language directly, but to try to bring your vocabulary up to date by taking advantage of such

[1] Readers who might think that the Major is exaggerating may like to refer to the source of his information: if it amuses them, they will find *"un jacquet"* on p. 81 of the *Mémento anglo-français,* by William Savage (with key to pronunciation and appendices). As for the *"harengs bouffis"* (bloaters), they may be found swimming about on p. 147 of *Travellers' Foreign Phrase Book,* by J. O. Ketteridge, F.S.A.A.

sojourns in Canada or Belgium as war or government missions may allow. But I must warn you of the dangers of such a system.

I had put my trust in the Canadians, who assure us that they are the only people in the world who speak pure French: the French of Montaigne. Yet I would not advise any of my compatriots to ask in a shoe shop for a pair of *"claques"* (smack in the face) if he wants snow boots, nor to ask a doorman for a *"char"* (Roman chariot) if he wants a taxi.

The Belgian experiment, if, as in my case, it precedes the stay in France, is even more dangerous. I remember the cunning expression of the house agent when I arrived in Paris from Liége and asked if he could find me an apartment *"à quatre places."* [2] "Facing the engine?" he inquired, and his smile showed me that I was now in the land of repartee.

No doubt about it, really good French must be learned in France. Surely the least I could do after marrying a Frenchwoman was to attempt to share her

[2] The Belgians say *"places"* where the French say *"pièces"* (rooms).

language. But, once on the spot, things became even more complicated. I knew already that there was one way of speaking French north of the Ardennes and another way south of it. I soon realized that there is one way of speaking French north of the Somme and another south of the Loire, a third east of the Massif Central, and (roughly) fifty-five other ways, so that in the end it is impossible to say exactly who in France speaks French. The citizens of Lyon make fun of those of Marseille, those of Bordeaux mock those of Lille or of the Landes, the inhabitants of Nice mock those of Toulouse, Parisians mock provincials, and all provincials make fun of the Parisians.

Determined to perfect my French, I set out on a long journey through France.

Experts had assured me that Touraine was the stronghold of perfect French, so I decided to take the waters at Touraine. When I returned to Paris my very British complexion (red marbled with blue veins) was distinctly heightened in color thanks to the Vouvray I had drunk, but when at my first dinner party I ventured to say of the *bourgueil* that it was very *gouleyant*—meaning that it slipped smoothly down your throat—they looked at me as if I were a Yahoo. Later in the evening, under the influence of the aforesaid *bourgueil*, I felt emboldened to tell Martine that she was as *ameugnounante*[3] as could be (which, for an ex-major in the Indian Army, was simply heroic), and all I got in the way of thanks was her inquiry: "Aren't you feeling well? No?"

Still resolved to try everything to make my French perfect, I continued my travels. Following up a certain sense of logical reasoning, I first went to visit the Tiberghiens at Roubaix, whom I had got to know during the war.

M. Tiberghien received me and said, not: "*Asseyez-vous*" ("Have a seat"), but: "*Mettez-vous*" ("Do put yourself").

At first I thought he meant to ask me if I had put on woolen underdrawers, but he merely repeated: "*Mettez-vous*," pointing to a chair. So I put myself in it.

A little later when I reached Marseille I heard M.

---

[3] An Angevin word (formed on "*mignon*") meaning "attractive."

Pappalardo exclaim as he saw me: "*Remettez-vous,* dear Madjor Tommepessonne." I thought he was about to bring me a restorative, but it was merely his way of inviting me to take a seat. So I re-put myself.

The French language varies with the longitude; yet it is true that most of the French understand one another more or less. However when a Basque starts speaking the language of his corner of the earth (and he seems to take a peculiar pleasure in doing so in the presence of a Parisian or a foreigner), then indeed you are in an impenetrable fog. After a brief stay in Bordeaux, where I learned that my laundry had gone to the *lisseuse* to be ironed, I was glad to get back to Paris; I felt more comfortable with Martine.

Do the Parisians know how to speak French or do they not? When at the Daninoses' I hear their little boy say to his sister: "*T'es pas cap de faire ça*" or whisper, looking at me (they must think I am more than a bit hard of hearing): "Did you notice his mustache? Funny sort of fur! And his imper? Impec!" [4] It is difficult for me

wwwwwwwwwwwwww

[4] "Imper": short for "impermeable" (mackintosh). "Impec": short for "impeccable" (nifty).

"Oh look Elmer! A statue of Ingrid Bergman!"

to believe that this is the language of Montesq (sorry, Montesquieu). At this rate, one may even wonder whether in fifty years' time France will not have lost half her vocabulary. You must admit that that would be "formid" (-able), but they are "cap" (-able) of doing it.

To return to adult Parisians, they would be almost comprehensible to the British if many of them did not feel obliged to garnish their sentences with Anglo-Saxon expressions which may be all right for the French but are all wrong for the British.[5]

The other evening in a drawing room I heard a good lady, whose words seemed to be emitted through her cigarette holder, declare to a man who was enveloped in smoke: "I was invited to the *previou* at the

---

[5] The Major is alluding to expressions like *"footing,"* which to the French means footing (walking), but means nothing at all to the English, or *smoking*, which to the British means smoking (a cigarette) and not a dinner jacket, to say nothing of the Parisian "English tearooms" which, like the one near the Porte Maillot, put up: *"Five o'clock à quatre heures."* In the same way, one might cite the case of many a Frenchman who, in England, having asked the way to the water closet, is surprised to be shown the kitchen, the smoking-room, or winter garden before discovering the lavatory.

Heïmarquett Ciateur in London. It was *auquai* [okay].
. . . But at the première here on Friday evening the
audience was simply lousy. Nothing but *plouks.*"

Plouks? Ploucs? Plouques? The Larousse dictionary
is no help here, but I think I gathered that they were
persons of no importance. In any case, they were not
des gens bien.

The smoke-engulfed gentleman was surprised (in
his own way):

"Jeannot wasn't there?"

"No, not Jeannot nor Marcel nor Jean. Nobody. It
was deadly."

Who were these Jeannots, Marcels, Jeans I was
always hearing about in Paris? An actor, a dramatist, and
a poet, all equally famous. Obviously this lady and
gentleman knew them very well. Yes, intimately, as did
three million other Parisians. It is smart in Paris to call
people by their Christian names as soon as they have
reached a certain degree of fame.

There again the French are the contrary of the
British: you can be friends with them for ten years and
they will still call you Monsieur Thompson, but they

readily use the Christian name for someone they do not know and never will. We who would not hesitate to call by their Christian names people we have known only for a few hours, without thereby becoming familiar, would hesitate to say "Larry" when we talk of Sir Laurence Olivier, unless, of course, we were friends of his.

However, there does exist a terrain on which, without quite meeting, the smart set of both countries can fight side by side: that of the *h*. To a superficial observer, England appears to be a united nation. In reality she has been divided for centuries by the war of the *h*.

One of the principal aspirations of the English elite is the aspirate *h*. An Englishman will go into training for twenty years to achieve the correct pronunciation of "Her Highness the Princess of Hanover." I have known some who have died without achieving it. To get even, the common people avoid sounding *h*'s where they do exist ("a nice 'ouse") and put them in in all sorts of places where they do not ("a hangel"); in France, where this war is far less virulent, a peculiar substitution (as with us) goes with it: the *e* becomes *a.*[6] Only a few days ago I heard an affected girl saying with what she hoped was an English accent:

"*J'â pris le thâ chez la Pochâ, c'étâ parfâ.*" Martine was good enough to translate and tell me that this distinguished person had taken tea with pleasure (I nearly wrote "*plasir*") with the Pochets. "*Parfait,*" moreover, is only one of a hundred very fashionable superlatives favored by these happy few to express appreciation of an evening, a film, or a play. The most often used are "*mhârvhailleux,*" "*dhivin,*" "*seûblime.*" The quintessence of chic seems to be to follow up these qualifications with the word "*quoi,*" or "what." A balletomane will say: "It's divine, what?"—which is his way of saying: "You're not going to think otherwise, no?" and also a way of dragging you along in his wake without waiting to hear what you have not had a chance to say.

By Jove! How the devil can an ex-major in the Indian Army grasp all these deuced shades of meaning? In this, as in other things, the French adore paradox.

᠁᠁᠁᠁᠁᠁᠁᠁

[6] "Rather" is pronounced "rathâ" (*Major's note*).

Speaking of a gnat lost in the middle of a Picasso canvas, they will say: "It's *henormous!*" thereby intending not a description, but some sort of compliment to the gnat. Yet the other day when the Eiffel Tower was being discussed, I heard a lady say: "I think it's a little dear."

The other evening I went to one of those little theaters where they were giving a play of the kind called "advanced" because you understand it only a long time afterwards. The dialogue was crawling with this sort of thing:

"*Est-ce un fantassin?*"

"*Non, c'est un hexagone.*"

At each of these pearls my neighbor, who was evidently an initiate, emitted a kind of cluck, or gallinaceous hiccough. I saw her in the interval surrounded by a group of connoisseurs who were freely indulging themselves in "*extrhaordinaire's*" and "*rhe-mâr-quhâble-quoi's.*" In this land of Descartes there exists an intelligentsia which can find illumination only in obscurity. Someone went past, however, some wretched *plouk* eager for enlightenment, who confessed that he had understood nothing.

"But why on earth," said my neighbor, "must you insist on understanding a thing? How horribly bourgeois!"

Strange land! The workers hurl abuse at the bourgeois. The intellectuals make fun of them. The aristocracy despises them. But those who are readiest to run down the bourgeois, and feel most affronted by the term when applied to themselves, are the bourgeois. And the best of it is that, from plumbers to peers, including explorers, journalists, and actors, the whole country, engulfed as it is in the universal wave of social security, grows more and more bourgeois every day.

France? A nation of bourgeois who try to prove that they are not by attacking those who are.

Chapter 11

WHEN THE FRENCH TRAVEL . . .

I shall always remember my visit to the stadium of Delphi. Not so much because of the majesty of the site still imbued with the Pythian mystery, but rather for the remark of a Frenchman on a cruise who, after running his eyes over it, partly for himself, partly to adjust his Kodak, partly for France, said to his wife:

"Doesn't it remind you, darling, of the Jean Bouin stadium at home?"

This strange reminiscence recalled to my memory countless similar remarks made by French people all over the world: those French tourists who discover the Passage du Havre at Milan, the Côte d'Azur in Florida, or Vézelay at St. James of Compostella. When an Englishman contemplates the Bay of Rio, or St. Peter's in Rome, he just thinks about St. Peter's or the Bay of Rio. Not having such a simple mind, a Frenchman will profit by the occasion to evoke the Bay of Naples or Chartres Cathedral.

When the English set off on their travels, they take with them a sponge bag, an umbrella, and (if they are going to France) a little spirit stove for making tea. Yet a customs official examining what is in their minds would find that they had nothing to declare. M. Taupin may sometimes forget his toothbrush, but he is always armed with a voluminous mental stock of comparisons against which, so far, all customs officials have been powerless to act.

Some time ago I visited Bruges with the Taupins. "It's extraordinary," said M. Taupin, "how much all this reminds me of Venice!"

Six months later in Venice, as our gondola after passing the Bridge of Sighs was making for the Fenice Theater, "Oh, Tounet," cried Mme Taupin, "look over there. Isn't it all just like Bruges?"

By dint of talking about Bruges in Venice and of Amsterdam in Copenhagen, the Taupins are now unable to say whether in 1949 they were on the Grand Canal or the Zuider Zee.

The quality of foreign dishes is also referred to the normal (i.e., the French) standard, especially as the comparison can nearly always be made to the advantage of the French (the only real) cooking. Sure of this supremacy, the French are unshakable in their demands. Mme Taupin would herself cheerfully instruct the natives about their specialties. While she is settling down to the *gnocchi alla romana,* she explains so fully how she prepares it *à la parisienne* that I do not know whether I am lunching in the Plazza Rusticucci or at the Place de l'Alma. M. Taupin, who is worried about his liver, thinks nothing is so difficult to find as plain cooking.

"Ah," he says, as if he were speaking of some dear friend, "this admirable soup!"

A Frenchman's nostalgic longing for French cooking when he is abroad has always impressed me. Is it only because the English do not know what it is to suffer

"Isn't it all just like Bruges?"

from this melancholy longing that they are able to colonize the whole world and settle anywhere without any regrets? Perhaps. . . .

A comparison machine for points of interest and the food of other countries, the Frenchman becomes a calculating-machine in hotels and shops. Mme Taupin has a way of using her husband as a currency-conversion apparatus which leaves me speechless. I treasure the memory of an afternoon specially devoted to footwear in the streets of San Sebastián.

"Two hundred and ninety-five pesetas, darling, what does that make?"

Darling explains that you must multiply by nine or by ten, according to the rate of exchange:

"About three thousand francs."

"When I think," muses Mme Taupin, "that the same thing in Paris would cost twice as much—at least!"

They went in. And bought. Then they met some other French people who had found the same thing at half price (in the south). The strange thing is that the more the article pleased Mme Taupin, the more favorable became the rate of exchange. With one particular pair of slippers I witnessed the fall of the peseta to 7.50, an unhoped-for affair that summer. On the other hand, M. Taupin was not so fortunate at Bilbao over a trench coat that pleased him but not Madame: the peseta suddenly soared to 12 francs.

"I don't want to stop you, Tounet, but really it's ridiculous—you'll find the same thing in Paris, only better and not so expensive. . . ."

Having compared basilicas with cathedrals, rios with canals, and pesetas with francs, the Frenchman then discovers fresh resources in comparison between himself and the aborigines. He looks at the world with an amused, often indulgent, and readily critical eye, inclined to scoff proportionately more as the currency of the country is less steady. To tell the truth, no one seems to him very down to earth: the Americans are grown-up children, the English golfers, the Italians spaghetti-eaters, the Spaniards toreadors, the South Americans perpetual summer vacationers. In his heart he is always asking: "How can a person possibly not be French?"

The Englishman does not ask himself the same question, at least not in the same way. He has learned once and for all that the world comprises Englishmen and various other tribes. In a universe that is becoming more and more mixed up—where you find Frenchmen in the Cocos Islands and Kanaks in Stockholm—the Englishman remains an Englishman and does not mix. Twenty-one miles of sea and a historical rampart of strict customs and costumes keep his island free from contamination. He himself, rarely subject to emotions or to head colds, travels across our planet like a miniature Great Britain in motion, inaccessible yet near, like his island. He is very much interested in the customs of all these curious *peoples,* and considers them with the explorative eye of a man who has been sent on a mission to the Zulus, sometimes even venturing to touch them experimentally with the tip of his stick or umbrella. Every now and then he is most surprised to discover among these individuals someone who really appears to be a gentleman. But instead of wondering how this man happened to be born an outlander, he muses simply: "What a pity it is he isn't British!"

A magic screen brings him an indirect, purified vision of the outside world: an invisible waterproof protects him from all external pollution: he emerges intact from the slums of Naples or the hordes of the Brahmaputra. The Frenchman, once outside of France, feels obliged to live up to his reputation of being a Don Juan from the land that for centuries has been honored as the capital of seduction. He wants to love and he wants to be loved. In his quality of propagator of the generous principles of 1789, he sets out in search of adventure in the native quarters. The Englishman, more reserved even than the natives, hurries off to a tearoom or to the British Club. At Bombay and at Caracas, at Havana and at Lucerne, everywhere he orients himself according to the cardinal points of his compass: bacon, tea, club, and whisky. When night falls, and with the help of the Almighty, he will sleep soundly in an alien land. He knows that at the slightest alarm he can count on his standing as a "British subject" as in an earlier time the Roman counted on the prerogative of his status: *civis Britannicus sum.* He is assured of this by a tragic yet reassuring passage in his phrase book under the heading

POLICE, COMPLAINTS: "I've had my wallet . . . bag . . . cloak . . . stolen. . . . Stop thief. . . . Fire! . . . Help! . . . Drive me to the British Consulate!" One can feel sure that at once the Foreign Office, Scotland Yard, and the Intelligence Service will be on their toes. Should the situation be aggravated and develop into a riot, it will be made known that H.M.S. *Revenge,* steaming at full speed toward Aden, is bringing protection to Mr. Smith.

Perhaps M. Taupin does not feel so sure about his consuls and their powers? While I detest bothering with papers, he loves to set out with a full set of letters of recommendation. Acquired at the cost of manifold negotiations, these credentials inform the Duke of Rovedrego, the Alcalde of Granada, or the Commendator Ruspolo di Ruspoli that M. Taupin is traveling for his pleasure. They are all, of course, important people, and, as they possess several residences, châteaux, or country houses, are always somewhere else. Never mind, with all these confounded letters—which will have no effect whatever upon the people they are addressed to, even when they do reach them—M. Taupin feels happier. "You never know," he says.

That is how M. Taupin travels. It would be more accurate to say that is how France travels. For M. Taupin exports the whole of France with him. An Englishman, convinced as he is of his superiority, contents himself with making his ascendancy felt (pretty disagreeably at times). The Frenchman is equally convinced of the superiority of his own country; but he personally is mad, witty France, gallant France, the France of freedom, Vercingetorix, Christian Dior, Pascal, and the rue de la Paix. He who, at home, seizes on any pretext for disparaging his body politic, who in Paris would rather buy a detective story signed W. A. Thorndyke than one signed J. Dupont,[1] now defends France, her artists, her inventors, with all the fervor of a crusader. And who would dream of attacking him? Hotel-managers, restau-

[1] M. Daninos confided to me that he became known far more quickly as the editor of Major Thompson than when he wrote under his own name (*Major's note*).

1 5 5

rant-keepers come to him to inhale a little Parisian air.[2] And M. Taupin receives them on his ambulant homeland with good-humored satisfaction. The restaurant-keeper says: "Ah, France!" and M. Taupin says: "Ah . . ." Then his interlocutor sighs: "Ah! Paris!" and M. Taupin replies: "Ah! . . ." And so from Ah! to Ah! the dialogue continues. The world disappears, only Paris remains.

"There's nothing like it!" says M. Taupin.

"I lived in the ruâ des Chiseaux," states the Italian.

"Ah," sighs M. Taupin, "the good old rue des Ciseaux!" (He confesses afterwards that it is the first time he ever heard of it.)

"*La Torre di Aiffel!*"

"Ah! the Eiffel Tower!"

"*Les Folies-Bergère!*"

A touching moment, when after a rather more lusty "*Ah!*" M. Taupin and the restaurant-keeper exchange a sly wink. Then M. Taupin, generous and chivalrous, concludes with:

"Every man has two countries, his own and France."

wwwwwwwwwwwww

[2] Abroad, every Frenchman comes from Paris (*Major's note*).

But the foreigner must be on his guard if one day he takes this saying literally and decides to become naturalized. He may be reminded pretty quickly that the second country is not the first, and if he does not like it . . .

After all, France for the French!

Chapter 12

FORTY MILLION SPORTIFS[1]

There are a number of excellent seasons for visiting France, but there is one that may very well give you a false impression: the period from about the 1st to the 25th of July. One of my first trips in France took place during that period. I had come from Gibraltar, crossed the Pyrenees, and was on my way to Paris when I was stopped by two gendarmes at a crossroads:

"You can't go through!" they said.

At that time I still retained the English habit of

[1] The Frenchman's rather derivative term for sports enthusiasts (*Major's note*).

never asking questions, so I complied without asking why. The sight of a grand array of police led me to suppose that a bandit was about to be rounded up. However, when I perceived a great crowd on the Route Nationale conversing gaily with the mounted police, I concluded that the occurrence must be something less dramatic. A column of armored cars halted on the other side of the crossroads led me to believe for a moment that the army was about to march by. Evidently this was not the case, because I soon heard the police captain say to a young lieutenant, who was showing his impatience by slapping his boot with his cane (though his men did not seem to mind at all):

"Maneuvers or no maneuvers, you can't go through!"

It was indeed clear that no one would get through, not the French with their armored cars, nor Major Thompson with his more vulnerable vehicle, nor even the gentleman who extricated his imposing person from his still more imposing automobile, police pass in hand, and was merely told:

"Do as the rest do. Wait!"

From all these indications I had deduced that all traffic was being held up to free the highway for the President of the Republic and his suite, when a great cry burst from countless throats:

"There they are!"

This singular plural led me to suppose for a moment that the Head of the State was about to appear with my Most Gracious Sovereigns, who were then in France. Imagine my surprise on seeing emerge, instead of Gracious Sovereigns, two male individuals gracelessly pumping bicycles, with innertubes and tires slung around their necks, clad in garish jerseys and the briefest possible shorts, covered with mud, and altogether rather a shocking sight. The spectators were kind enough to explain to me—without my asking—that these fellows were cycling in the Tour de France and were getting to Paris as quickly as possible by the slowest roads, which seemed to me strange. But, after all, these are things about which an Englishman, who is never astonished at anything, should not express any tactless surprise. Occasionally in London a citizen may, from love of sport or to satisfy some whim, walk down Piccadilly in a red

"Maneuvers or no maneuvers, you can't get through!"

blazer and white shorts, but it would be the worst kind of bad taste to turn around and stare at him. Everyone is free to act and dress as he pleases without fear of being noticed in a country where good taste demands that one should see people without observing them.

What amazed me in this instance was not so much the negligent dress of these men, as the fact that the police brought all traffic to a standstill for them—for them and also for a line of lorries belonging to suppliers of *pâté* and *apéritifs* which at first sight had nothing to do with the proceedings but were actually—as inquiry revealed—intimately associated. I know that there is the same sort of Tour of England, but how different! Our racing cyclists, far from stopping the traffic, follow it; they stop at red lights like everyone else. They are only amateurs who apologize for passing one another and get off their bicycles to have tea. Above all, these young men, whom hardly anyone notices anyway, are properly dressed.[2]

[2] The Major is anxious to emphasize in this connection that "shorts," though they have the same meaning as "*courts*" in French,

.　　.　　.

I did not reach Paris till late that night. I was worried about the situation in Bengal, where—for reasons too long to explain, which besides are nobody else's affair— I had found it necessary to leave Ursula. There were threats of an uprising in Calcutta, the police had had to open fire on the mob, and eventually two hundred had been killed.

I had already heard that much in Gibraltar; but I wanted to know more. So I bought the Late Night edition —in fact, the Special Late Night edition—of an evening paper whose banner headline announced:

GARRALDI AND BIQUET FACE JUDGES TOGETHER

Thinking that an important courtroom trial was drawing to its close, I prepared to read the speeches un-

――――――――――

are nevertheless long. When a rugby-player's knickers are torn in a scrum and have to be replaced at once, the player is immediately surrounded by members of his team according to a very carefully prepared technique which leaves no chink for indiscreet eyes to penetrate. With the French, on the contrary, this technique of surrounding is far more lax and, according to the Major, constitutes an invitation to see a bit more than one would have cared to otherwise.

der the mouth-watering subtitle: *Florentine demon be-trayed by his servants,* when my eye was attracted to a cross-section map of the Pyrenees spread across the lower part of the paper. I learned later that Garraldi and Biquet were the heroes of the Tour de France, and that by "judges" one should understand—by one of those meta-phors so dear to the hearts of the French sports writers —two difficult mountain passes. The "demon" was a cyclist who happened to be wearing a red sweater, and the "servants" his team mates. As for the two hundred dead in Calcutta, they were buried in four lines under the Pyrenees mountains.

Therefore, I can only advise my countrymen, if they are desirous of keeping informed about events in the world at large, and in the Commonwealth in particular, not to come to France in July unless they are prepared to see the Commonwealth submit to the humiliating tyranny of racing bicycles.[3]

[3] An impassioned debate opened at this moment between the Ma-jor and his French collaborator when the latter recalled that one day when he was passing through London, feeling very worried about the international situation, he had been alarmed by a newspaper heading that summed it up in these terms:

A few days later when I spoke of the Tour de France to my friend Colonel Turlot, confessing that I could not understand the first thing about it, he retaliated by revealing that after having made three attempts to understand something about a cricket match he had had to undergo a lengthy tête-à-tête with a psychiatrist. He added:

"Do you know, my dear Thompson, that every day millions of '*sportifs*' follow the Tour?"

ENGLAND'S DESPERATE POSITION

which to a Frenchman meant: *L'Angleterre dans une situation désespérée.* An illuminating subtitle, *In spite of 6–3 be proud of old England,* shed a strange light on the question. The Major's collaborator thought that a grave decision had been taken. Then his eye was caught by the little square reserved for special bulletins, where he read:

TEST SCORES

ENGLAND: FIRST INNINGS 435, HUTTON 169, COMPTON 64. RAMADIN 6-113, ATKINSON 3-78, FALL OF WICKETS: 1-1, 2-12, 3-16, ETC.

which explained everything.

On making inquiries, the desperate situation was England's plight in football, when for the first time in ninety years she had been beaten by Hungary (6–3). And the extra editions concerned cricket.

"How can you," said the Major, "compare an historic match which was such a national humiliation, with your confounded bicycle race?"

The Major's face having become purple in a symptomatic fashion, it seemed better to avoid an explosion and close the discussion.

"Do you mean, my dear Tiourlott, that they follow the competitors on their bicycles?"

M. Turlot looked at me as if he thought I was joking. No. Certainly the *"sportifs"* he spoke of exercised themselves every day, but only in buying the Special Late Extra, or in arranging to have a good place to see the finish in Paris.

I discovered there a fresh and fundamental difference between our two countries; the English call themselves sportive when they practice some sport. The French call themselves sportive when they look on. So that, painful as the truth may seem to my countrymen, there are *more sportsmen in France than in England.* Moreover, it could not be said that the French sports spectator is not a sportsman. Even at the cinema, especially at the time of the Tour de France, M. Charnelet is really there for a workout. After the news, there he is, obliged to climb on his bicycle and to cover seven hundred kilometers of the route (for, though the competitors cover only one lap at a time, the spectator has to absorb five or six, and, whether he wants to or not, has to climb Mt. Galibier and descend the Col d'Albos).

M. Charnelet, whose wishes have not been consulted, is obliged to keep on, over the frightful cobblestones of Normandy; he has a puncture in the neighborhood of Longwy, skids, sets off again, though he has dropped behind, kisses an Alsatian girl on the way, in spite of his boils, climbs up the treacherous hairpin bends of Mt. Ventoux, and as a final penalty crosses the desolate waste land of Crau.

There is nothing so exhausting as to be forced to cross Crau in a cinema on the Champs-Élysées at ten thirty in the evening. The group of cyclists straggles, the group dawdles, the group re-forms, the group gets mixed up. It is conservatively estimated that fifteen million Frenchmen mentally compete in this contest, and each feels that he has the legs—what did I say?—I mean the golden flexed muscles of Garraldi, or the "Demon of the Hills," or the relentless calves of Biquet, that plucky little Frenchman whose luck so often deserts him but who can perform miracles at the critical moment.

· · ·

In stadiums, at the ringside, or around tennis courts, the French have a way of gesticulating, shouting, and generally getting themselves worked up, which contrasts pretty strongly with the attitude of a normal Englishman. Compare a boxing-match in France with one in England. At first glance, they look like the same sport. In reality, they are two very different things. England was the cradle of boxing and many other sports. Boxing, tennis, football, golf are all English offspring. With the passage of time they have become emancipated, they have traveled, they have been made to marry beneath them. Their essential purity has been polluted. Between those elderly English spinsters who in order to see the Wimbledon finals spend the night on camp stools discussing Drobny's drop shot or Rosewall's backhand as they would a stitch in knitting, and the young French fans around the Roland-Garros courts who call faults *"carottes"* and lobs *"chandelles"* (especially if it is a foreigner who makes them), there is an almost interstellar difference. No matter! Whatever Colonel Turlot may say, the sport's ancestors are English.[4] The noble art of

ᴧᴧᴧᴧᴧᴧᴧᴧᴧᴧᴧᴧᴧᴧᴧᴧᴧ

[4] Colonel Turlot, who was present, violently attacked the Major at this point. Armed with a Larousse dictionary, he dealt him a shattering lexicographic blow. " 'Cricket,' " he read feverishly, " 'favorite exer-

delivering blows and avoiding them was already honored under William the Conqueror, while the French were still defending Paris with their feet. Today what happens? In England the main event takes place in the ring. In Paris they fight in the auditorium. In England you could hear a pin drop. In France you would not hear a machine gun. In England gentlemen in dinner jackets gravely discuss the great value of evasive action, and the referee is respected like a god. In France the only thing that is respected is a frontal attack, and the referee is denounced, insulted, and abused as an enemy. Finally, while the French hurl sarcastic taunts at the weaker combatant, the English encourage him.

ᴡᴡᴡᴡᴡᴡᴡᴡᴡᴡᴡᴡ

cise of the English, is in reality only a modification of the ancient French game of *la crosse*. Is sometimes written in the French fashion, *criquet*—' "

"Ridiculous!" cried the Major.

" 'Golf,' " continued the Colonel, with the utmost calm, " 'very possibly owes its origin to the old French game *le mail.*' "

"Preposterous! Absurd!" sneered the Major.

" 'Tennis,' " continued the Colonel with imperturbability, " 'developed out of the old French game *la longue paume.*' "

"Everyone knows that lawn tennis was invented by my forebear Major Wingfield in 1874," exploded the Major, getting very red, and to avoid worse happenings he went off to get some tea.

"Tea," he emphasized, slamming the door.

. . .

This respect for the weaker competitor and the almost instinctive desire to give him a fighting chance are the unwritten laws of the realm, and are obeyed in the same way by fishermen and huntsmen. To discredit someone for ever, an Englishman will say of him: "He's shooting a sitting bird." I am shocked by the suggestion that in France the rule which says that a bird on the ground must not be shot at is not always respected. I have been told this, though of course I don't believe it.[5]

An Englishman's fishing is directed by the same rigid code. On parts of the Test, one of the noblest waters in Hampshire, it would be a crime to fish at sunset; at the very moment when the light fades and the trout begin to rise and become "easier," the gentleman, having spent the day in torrid heat lying in wait for a fish, packs up and goes back to London. Need I add that to use a worm for bait is a dreadful crime, and that the pseudo-sportsmen who use a wet fly rather than a dry are looked at askance?

I do not doubt that French sportsmen are moved by

---

[5] A rather hypocritical remark, as the Major does believe it.

"It's amazing what a few days in England did to Jules!"

an equal desire for fairness. Yet they are so different! When an Englishman lands the salmon of his life, he has it stuffed. The Frenchman eats it, after being photographed with his catch. If an Englishman catches an undersized trout, he throws it back. A Frenchman would prefer to eat it. The Frenchman always eats what he catches, not because he is hungry, but because of that fear of being ridiculous if he comes home empty-handed which affects us English so little and positively torments the French, and because any amusement seems silly to him if it does not serve some purpose.

Such utilitarian preoccupations do not affect us; but it is repugnant to the French to do things which are not useful. (I have been told that they have three children rather than two not through carelessness but because of the family allowance.) A father makes his son learn English, not for the beauty of the language (always a relative affair in the eyes of a Frenchman), but because it may be useful later on (*cela peut lui servir plus tard*). In the Turlot family there is always one son learning German so that he can become an interpreter in time of war.

Unlike the French, the English adore doing things that, strictly speaking, serve no purpose. It is only in affairs of the heart that they hate doing anything superfluous, like paying court.[6] Or even making love. But as soon as it is a question of some serious enterprise like fishing or shooting, the most ordinary Englishman will ruin himself by expending vast reserves of uselessness for the love of sport.

Much more could be said about the way sport is treated by the English and mistreated by the French. I now perceive that, after having written a great deal, I have said nothing about the sport which the greatest number of Frenchmen enjoy (two million of them as against two hundred thousand who play bowls). I mean motoring. That in itself calls for special consideration and deserves to be studied in some quiet corner where one can meditate on the subject without any risk of being run over.

---

[6] The French may be indifferent fishermen, yet they are masters in the art of playing their catch when they are courting a woman, and they are unequaled in getting what they want with women by discussing Proust or Cinemascope (*Major's note*).

Chapter 13

FRANCE AT THE WHEEL

Beware of the French in general, but particularly on the road.

It is essential for an Englishman arriving in France to realize at once that there are two kinds of Frenchmen: pedestrians and drivers. The pedestrians loathe the drivers, and the drivers terrorize the pedestrians, though the first pass instantaneously into the camp of the second the moment they get their hands on a steering-wheel. (It is the same at the theater with late-comers: after disturbing a dozen people to get to their seats, they are the first to protest about those who have the cheek to arrive later.)

The English drive badly but prudently. The French drive well but madly. The proportion of accidents in the two countries is about the same. But I feel more comfortable with people who do good things badly, than with those who do bad things well.

The English (and Americans) have long been convinced that a car travels less rapidly than an airplane.

The French (and most of the Latins) still seem determined to prove the contrary.

In the heart of many a Frenchman there slumbers a racing-driver ready to be awakened by the mere contact of his foot with the accelerator. The peaceful citizen who graciously invited you into his car can be metamorphosed before your very eyes into a demoniacal steersman. Jerome Charnelet, father of a family, a man who would not squash a fly on a windowpane, is quite ready to flatten out one pedestrian per mile provided he feels he has *the right of way*. At the green light he sees red. Then nothing slows him down, not even the amber one. On the road, this man who has a reputation for steadiness steadily refuses to make way for anyone. It is only when he is absolutely forced to, after having received a sustained barrage of horn-blowing, that he will sullenly relinquish the middle of the road. The English keep to the left. Most nations keep to the right. The French favor the middle.

The mere fact that someone has passed him puts M. Charnelet in a vile temper. He recovers his serenity only when he passes some new rival. Meanwhile, his entire family has to behave with complete decorum. Woe betide Mme Charnelet if, when asked for it, she cannot find in the car the "Southern Half of France" which he left behind on the drawing-room mantelpiece. Woe betide her if she does not respond instantly to the question: "Avallon-Châlons, how far?" Even if she does answer, M. Charnelet, five foot eight of sadism once his foot is on the accelerator, is already enjoying the pleasure he will get out of proving that her calculations are wrong. The children, too, are well trained: "When your father's thirsty, you'll have a drink." Above all, no untimely stops. "You should have done it before," says M. Charnelet. They suffer in silence out of respect for that all-powerful goddess of the average Frenchman: Average Speed.

When an English motorist prepares to do three hundred miles in England, he fully intends to do three hundred miles.

When a Frenchman gets into his car to do six hundred kilometers, two thirds of his mind is taken up with his average speed, the other third is filled with asterisks and forks. I mean those famous hieroglyphics in his beloved Michelin guide. His dream, after having kept up an average of ninety kilometers an hour for three hours, is to find a restaurant ✗✗✿✿✿ if possible in a site ★★★ near a 🛏 (reliable) to verify the spark plugs and the oil.

The Englishman will just allow himself to think about a good 🛏 after drinking some good *t*. That is, if he stays in England. If he goes to France, he must first of all force himself to drive on the right side of the road, which in his eyes is the wrong side. That is the most delicate problem. The French have a way of keeping to the right, while continually sliding to the left, which strongly recalls their leanings in politics: the stanchest conservatives refuse to be called "right" at any price. That is why when an English motorist gets to France, he has some difficulty in knowing where to drive. In reality, he would have to push on to Kenya before again meeting normal people who drive on the left, calculate in miles, use avoirdupois weights and measures, and whose normal temperature is 98.6.[1] Meanwhile, he must accustom himself to that monotonous metric-system zone, which leaves no room for the glorious uncertainty of our old measures: ounce, bushel, or peck. A kilometer is always one thousand stupid meters, whereas with us the mile is marvelously eight furlongs, a furlong two hundred and twenty yards, a yard three feet, a foot twelve inches. . . . It is true that the *Perfect Travellers' Pocket-Book* puts things right by reminding him that to transfer centigrade into Fahrenheit "you merely multiply by 9, divide by 5, and add 32 degrees." As for converting kilometers into miles, that is even easier: "Multiply by 5 and divide by 8."[2]

---

[1] Fahrenheit, of course.

[2] Once again, the Major is not inventing. These practical hints are given in the *Travellers Foreign Phrase Book*, by J. O. Ketteridge, F.S.A.A., for the use of the English, already mentioned, p. 134, note 1.

During one of my first tours in France, when I was suffering from the combined effects of a bad chill and a bad sea, I decided to stop at a hotel in Calais and take my temperature. As the thermometer registered only 40.3, I set out again in all confidence, putting the top of my car down, and was rolling pleasantly along with the windscreen open when I remembered I was among these deuced Continentals who can never do anything like anybody else. I immediately applied myself to converting my continental temperature into Fahrenheit, and kilometers into miles.

I was about to multiply 274 by 5, to divide by 9, and add 32 degrees to the distance between Calais and Paris when the sight of another car coming in the opposite direction on the same side of the road as myself made me suddenly realize that, lost as I was in my calculations, I had forgotten to drive on the right. I changed over to the right and braked in time, while my vis-à-vis, pulling up beside me, shouted point blank: "Completely cracked, you old idiot? Think you're still with the *rosbifs*?"

Then, taking my silence for incomprehension, he let in the clutch and looked at me, tapping his forehead with his forefinger.

I was soon to learn that this gesture is a veritable rite.

Many a time since then I have been on the road with M. Taupin or M. Charnelet and have seen them, for reasons frequently obscure, glare at a motorist they were passing and tap their foreheads. Very often he who has just been passed catches up with M. Taupin and, for a no less mysterious motive, addresses him in the same dumb language, though this time he uses his first finger like a kind of screwdriver on his temple. I have deduced from this that the French spend their time on the roads asking themselves whether they are mad and nearly always find someone at hand to convince them that they are.

It is curious to note that a large number of people who, armed with the approved dictionary, are ready to do battle for their idea of "correct" language, are apt to lose all verbal restraint and all sense of propriety as soon

as they are in a car.[3] The French, who are born syn-
tacticians as others are born navigators or musicians,
care nothing for syntax the moment they are at the
wheel.

In this land of moderation it is always surprising
to see people losing their self-control. But that they lose
it with their hands on the wheel may be pregnant with
grave consequences. At least one must do them this
justice; you hear them coming a long way off. The golden
rule for English motorists is to pass unnoticed. The
Frenchman's aim is rather to alarm people on the road
until he has cleared everyone else out of sight. To
achieve this he makes as much noise as possible. Most of
the world's motorcars run on petrol. French cars run on
their horns. Especially when they are forced to stop.[4]

[3] It is easy to see, then, why the French were so surprised by the
public apology which appeared lately in the agony column of *The
Times,* from a repentant motorist to one of his countrymen on whom
he had launched a rather violent epithet. A Frenchman would rather
have sought to catch up with his adversary and say a bit more, or by
means of some skillfully executed wobbling make him collide with a
plane tree.

[4] This is an undisguised allusion to Paris blocks. With the English,
honking means making an improper noise. The horn, whose use in
France is a duty or a pastime, can be used in England only in emer-

The French spend their time on the roads asking themselves whether they are mad and nearly always find someone at hand to convince them that they are

.　　.　　.

One might think that the Frenchman's appetite for speed was determined by the horsepower of his car. This is an error. The smaller his car, the faster he wants to go. In this land of paradox the least dangerous cars are the most powerful ones: their drivers, having become blasé, are the only ones who enjoy the luxury of driving "with a reserve of power" and of accelerating without forcing the gas pedal to the floorboards.

As for Frenchwomen, one must do them this justice: they drive more slowly than the men. An Englishman might therefore logically believe he would be safer with them. This is another error. In a country where everyone goes so fast, this very slowness constitutes a

gency. I was in the Major's *Austin of England* in London one day when I felt I should like to smoke. By accident, instead of pressing the cigarette-lighter, I leaned on the horn. I was at once overwhelmed with withering glances from ten pairs of eyes (not counting the Major's). I wished I could have hidden under the hood.

On the road, the English driver, sacrificing safety to courtesy, never takes his eyes off the rear-view mirror. If he sees another car preparing to pass him, he waves him on as soon as the road is clear. No need for a horn. Of course there are the cars coming in the opposite direction at a turn of the road. But they would die rather than honk. Very often they do die in this way.

most terrible danger. Add to that a certain variability in pace, and that charming spirit of indecision from which one may deduce from a flashing-light signal on the left side that the driveress is going to turn right (though even this is not absolutely certain), and one may realize that there is nothing so hazardous as being driven by a woman.

There exists, however, a super-danger in this country where, as in many others, women do not know how to drive or how to smoke. That is, women who smoke while they are driving. The safest thing to do if you have the misfortune to be threatened by this charming calamity is to stop at the nearest town and take the train.

Chapter 14

LOVELY SUNDAYS

It is not inconceivable to suppose that if England has not been invaded since 1066 it is because foreigners are afraid of spending a Sunday there.

If you compare the English Sunday, which imposes boredom, with the French Sunday, which imposes amusement, you may well wonder which of the two is the more grisly.

Many Frenchmen spend the weekdays asking themselves what they will do on Sunday. Sunday usually arrives before they have found an answer. At least, that is what happens with the Taupins and the Robillards, who have often confessed to me that they have no idea what to do on Sunday.

People never suffer from this sort of indecision in England, where there is hardly anything else to do on Sunday but think about what there is to be done in the week.

To tell the truth, I know no more miserable spectacle than M. Robillard's Sabbath expression as he pushes his latest-born in his pram along the Champs-Élysées, cuffing his eldest because he crossed the road alone, dragging along his little girl who does not want to cross at all, calling out to Mme R. who is fatally drawn to the shopwindows: "Are you coming, yes or no?" and at last reaching the Bois in the middle of a procession of walkers whose expression is curiously—I nearly wrote "furiously"—like his own. All these people who are walking walk until they reach a certain point, where they stop, sit down, and begin looking at the people who are walking toward other points, while those in motion watch those who are seated watching them passing by.

On Sunday, half of France looks at the other half.

Parisians dressed up in country clothes visit friends in the country disguised for the occasion in their town clothes. The former are astonished at the sight of so much dark serge and so many white collars amid the cows and clover; the latter observe with some mistrust these pseudo-English in their tweeds and open shirts.

In the late afternoon, those driving back from the country survey with some contempt the walkers who have had to spend their day in the Bois de Boulogne, and who in turn grin jeeringly at the agglutinated procession of cars, asking themselves whether one does not have to be a bit dotty to join a queue on a super-highway. Meanwhile, the mass of *"sportifs"*—those who go to the horse races and who fail to understand how anyone can spend a Sunday watching people kick a ball about, and those in the stadiums who wonder what pleasure there can be in putting a person's money in the care of horses—become momentary allies in a general contempt for their fellow citizens who waste their time on the highways and the avenues.

Throughout the summer the Paris concierges sit on cane-bottomed chairs drawn outdoors from their lairs and lie in wait for, comment upon, and check those returning home.

A few individualists, moved by a spirit of contradiction rather than by any deep-rooted taste, decide to stay at home to hammer on nails, put things in order which they get out of order, or devote themselves to the national sport of "puttering around," which consists essentially in manufacturing out of old junk and with an expenditure of immense toil articles that can be bought brand-new and cheaply over the counter. ("Puttering around" constitutes an activity in France which is so important that it deserves special consideration, and I shall come back to it.) These partisans of Sunday-at-home correspond in a certain sense to the mass of British citizens who busy themselves with their gardens or with devouring divorce items in the thick Sunday newspapers, and with lunching as badly as on any other day, only eating rather more.

In his inscrutable caprice the Creator has made us opposite from our neighbors right up to the last second of the seventh day.

France and England both have two faces, a week-day face and a Sunday face; but France shows hers while England doesn't.

On Sundays the Frenchman is careful about his dress. The Englishman neglects his. While his French neighbor "dresses," his tendency is rather to undress.[1] On Sundays the Frenchman shaves more carefully. The Englishman—no, there are no two ways of shaving for an Englishman.

While my compatriots get through this day of immobility at home wearing their shabbiest clothes, leaving it to a few uneducated *nouveaux riches* to dress correctly, the French, all spruced up, come out of their houses to flaunt themselves in their finest attire: *le costume du dimanche.* There is no question of Sunday clothes for an Englishman, unless he is entirely without friends or modesty—which is rare.

The height of *chic* for a Frenchman is to be *tiré à quatre épingles,* an expression which, like *s'endiman-*

---

[1] Except to go to church, if he does go. Generally, and in small towns particularly, the English go to church not so much for the sake of going as to see who did not go (*Major's note*).

We English look more natural dressed as golfers

cher, has no real equivalent in the language of Shake-speare.[2] Compared with the Englishman, who still maintains a sporting air in a *smoking,*[3] the Frenchman maintains a certain formality in sporting-clothes, and often in plus fours he does not seem to be quite real. Perhaps it is because he is insufficiently trousered.

After all, one must know what one is before know-ing what one wants to become. We English had been playing golf for five hundred years when in 1635 the French Academy was founded. Is it not all to the honor and to the advantage of the French that they look more natural dressed up as Academicians than as golfers?

Differing from his neighbor on the globe, who likes to shine like a new penny, the Englishman has a horror of anything new and considers it counterfeit. For him true *chic* is inseparable from a certain indefinable aura of shabbiness. Formerly, in the days when Frenchmen

[2] The English expressions "dressed up to the nines" or "just stepped out of a bandbox," so difficult to translate, have a slightly derogatory meaning which the French do not (*Major's note*).

[3] I mean, of course, a dinner jacket, but in France one must write English as the French do (*Major's note*).

gave their slightly worn clothes to their servants, the English dandies used to make their butlers wear their new suits to break them in. Today the *Belgravia boys*[4] wear their new suits in secret until they are fit to be seen. The Frenchman will wear his old things until they are absolutely threadbare and keep his new suit for Sunday.

The English way of living six days a week and dying each Sunday may surprise a foreigner, but that of many Frenchmen who merely exist during the week to burst forth on Sundays is no less astonishing.

This anxiety to preserve new things and to make use of them only in extremities (week-ends) is doubtless one of the characteristics of the Frenchman, who perhaps fears that he might get rusty if he did not polish himself up once a week.

My visit to the Turlots was to reveal other aspects of the careful and foreseeing French.

[4] Expression coined by the Major to indicate males of the district around Belgrave Square, one of the smartest quarters of London.

Chapter 15

DIABOLICAL INVENTIONS OF
THE FRENCH

The first time I arrived in Saumur at my friends the Turlots', one lovely summer's day, their house in the rue Dacier appeared quite tomblike, with all its shutters fast closed. The servant who opened the door immediately made me put on some peculiar felt slippers, perhaps to protect the parquet floor, but more likely to make me lose my balance. Then she ushered me into a fairly large salon impregnated with the smell of must and cretonne. Although the sun filtered through the shutters, I had to accustom my eyes to the semi-darkness before I could penetrate the surrounding mystery. On all sides were white shapes. One could with difficulty discern the forms of several armchairs, a sofa, a grand piano, a chest, something that resembled a harp—all swathed in dust sheets. A number of pictures hung on the walls, but it was difficult to know what they represented. Not because they belonged to the modern school of painting, but because they were covered with newspaper. The only thing that seemed animated by any life of its own was the clock. And even its tick-tock came from under a white shroud penetrated by the arrow of a bronze Cupid. In a corner over a little table hung two crossed cavalry sabers, protected by sheaths of yellow linen. I had evidently come at a bad moment: the Turlots were moving. Or they had fallen on evil days and were selling their belongings. The furniture was about to be carted away. My pessimistic suppositions were ended by the appearance of a gray dust sheet from which emerged the head of the Colonel: "Forgive me, my dear Major, I was puttering around."

I have often wondered what the Colonel's "puttering" really amounted to. I was often to find my way into what he called his "lab" and see him busy with an oscil-

lator and a kind of condenser without ever, until recently, guessing what kind of experiments he was con-
ducting. Now I think I can declare that the masterpiece
he has been working on for the last seven years is a wireless set, every bit of which he has assembled with his
own hands. It has cost him more than 40,000 francs. On
fine days he can hear the program from the Massif Central. He could get the whole world on a set costing
2,270 francs in any wireless shop. Only a stupid Englishman could fail to notice the difference.

Colonel Turlot's puttering is of the usual handy-man
variety, but there also exists a de-luxe puttering, the
kind practiced by M. Charnelet upon his car. As soon
as he has bought a car, M. Charnelet has one aim: to
make it look less like a standard model. With the help of
innumerable dealers—each of whom sells him some little
gadget, a turn-indicator or a rear-view mirror, saying:
"With that it's not just anybody's car" [1]—M. Charnelet

----

[1] Excellent example of the discrepancy between advertising and
salesmanship in this country where they are always telling you: *"Faites
comme tout le monde,"* but end by persuading you to do as nobody

adorns it with all sorts of accessories until, with the radiator grille changed, it is unrecognizable. Early on office hours—he secludes himself and his car in the Bois de Boulogne, brings out his duster, rubs the chromium, polishes the paintwork, and is outwardly annoyed but secretly delighted when an idler prowls around it and finally asks what make it is.

Besides this puttering de luxe, there is the ordinary, everyday variety of puttering which is even more fascinating to study: it forms an integral part of the life of every individual. Among its typical manifestations figures the filter, or, more precisely, the coffee-filter. I have often wondered why the Frenchman, who could have set before him, ready and hot, the best coffee in the world, prefers to see it drip drop by drop through a mysterious alembic and finally drink it cold, after burning his fingers in an unsuccessful attempt to regulate the

else would ever dream of doing. French people have a horror of being noticed because they have an abject fear of being ridiculous, but do everything they can to avoid passing unnoticed. The fear of seeming ridiculous (which could not affect an Englishman, as, being English, he could not be ridiculous) curbs them, but the desire for manifesting their individuality spurs them on (*Major's note*).

One lovely summer's day

filtering-mechanism. I can only suppose that he likes to "putter" with coffee.[2] The filter is one of those discoveries, one of those diabolical inventions of the French, which include the *"Minuterie"* (time-limited electric-light switches), the concierge, the automatically closing subway doors, unperforated money-order blanks, scissors for snipping unperforated money-order blanks, restrictive electric-light switches that give one a choice between a ceiling light without the bedside light or a bedside light without the ceiling light, and all those creaking cages or cabins which it is very rash to board without reading the INSTRUCTIONS FOR OPERATING, and which, under the name of lifts, achieve the noble distinction of remaining the one means of locomotion slower than walking.

Of all the diabolical inventions of the French, one deserves the palm: I refer to those places which the

[2] It is the same with books. Any English or American publisher who thought of forcing buyers to cut each book's pages along the top and down the side would soon be bankrupt. In France, on the contrary, certain publishers who wished to make an innovation and present already-cut books to the public, had to revert quickly to the old formula which alone could satisfy *real readers* (*Major's note*).

French, who love a paradox, call "conveniences" and which they have with great ingenuity rendered the most inconvenient in the world.[3] First, those in Paris cafés— so intimately associated with the telephone booth that one is sometimes not quite sure what kind of communication one is expected to establish. (The sight of a pale saucer in the middle of which a twenty-franc piece appeals desperately for a sister coin reminds you that you are in the Realm of the Tip.) The country ones—tiny cells that you reach only after fighting your way through a no-man's-land of hens and scrap iron—are obscure abysses where you keep your balance only by an acrobatic miracle and where you need all the cunning of a Red Indian to escape the blind vindictiveness of that maelstrom which, in the guise of a flushing, makes you bolt for a door so constructed that, instead of opening onto the dry, clean light of day, it recoils and pushes you back into the damp darkness.

wwwwwwwwwwww

[3] Obviously I would not broach such a subject in England, but as I am in the country of Rabelais, I think I can have a crack at it (*Major's note*).

.　　.　　.

Excuse this short absence from my subject. It was necessary. I now come back to Saumur and Colonel Turlot
and his dust sheets and his great works. Having covered up one of the strange machines in his "lab" with a
camouflage sheet probably scrounged from some Allies
Surplus Depot, the Colonel took off his overalls and hung
them on a nail. Then, extracting his watch from its case,
he exclaimed: "Good Lord, twelve o'clock already! Have
you seen my wife?"

We went to look for her. I thought the Colonel was
about to produce his wife from a dust sheet when half
of Mme Turlot emerged from a cupboard. Clad in blue
overalls, with her head tied up in a scarf, she was putting
a tailor-made suit with an astrakhan collar in a moth-
proof bag.

"Madame's latest extravagance," said the Colonel.
"Of course she doesn't wear it here except on special
occasions. It's really for going to Paris."

Mme Turlot begged me to excuse her. She really
was not presentable. She was going to put on a dress
and get ready for lunch. I was sorry that my arrival had

Temporarily out of order

thrown the household into a state of some perturbation. The Turlots, who have a large house, were preparing to lunch in the kitchen, but in my honor undertook to de-shroud the dining-room and the haunted salon with its spectral furniture, where they never ventured when they were alone.

"We'll open a nice bottle for you, my dear Major," said the Colonel, who possesses a very good cellar but every day drinks ordinary red wine.

It may seem dangerous to judge a country by appearances, especially when they are hidden under a dust sheet, but I have no doubt that the French in general make a less systematic use of the dust sheet than the Turlots do. But leaving aside the Colonel, I cannot help remembering that M. Taupin, like M. Charnelet, has only one thought when he buys a car: to put in seat covers. He removes them the day he sells the car (*perf. cond.*) and, if possible, uses them again in his new one.

I am inclined to believe that the dust cover is the symbol of the thrifty—even self-depriving—spirit of the French. These people, who are so greedy of possessions that they will say: "I have my poor," [4] and are more spoiled by life than any others on earth, make a veritable cult of hardship, and covering up the seats of their cars is one of its most widespread manifestations. I know of a millionaire who made a reputation by taking his meals on a kitchen table, sending his children to the village school, traveling third class, never cutting a piece of string, and saying to any of his employees who asked for a raise: "I can't imagine how you manage to spend so much!"

In this land of plenty the real, most solid wealth attires itself in humility: only the poor spend recklessly.

~~~~~~~~~~~~~~~~~~~~

[4] Compare this expression with the "I always give to the Salvation Army" loudly proclaimed by M. Charnelet when a salvationist in a blue bonnet comes into the restaurant. Obviously M. Charnelet wants to emphasize his discernment in giving. Direct contact with a down-and-out, especially in a restaurant, makes him uneasy, but the uniform of the Salvation Army is reassuring: he knows where his money goes (*Major's note*).

Chapter 16

THE LAND OF MIRACLES

The miracle, along with the vine, is one of the principal products of France.

All Frenchmen—whether they are positivists, rationalists, or Voltairians—firmly believe in miracles. When the enemy is at the gates of Paris, or when there is only a minute of play left against England at Colombes, then they rely on Providence, who, it must be admitted, has been damned good to them.

Having, like her Latin sisters, subscribed to miracles from her earliest childhood, France attracts miracles as other countries attract fog. More than that, she adapts them to the needs of the moment: the miracle that went on foot with Saint Geneviève, on horseback with Joan of Arc, became motorized with the taxis of the Marne. Tomorrow it may be propelled by atomic power.

In other countries, when a statesman cries: "Only a miracle can save us," the country is finished. In France it can be the beginning of great things. The Frenchman brightens up in darkness, becomes organized in chaos. Possible things do not interest him very much; impossible things fascinate him. In a land of facility any difficulty is inspiring. The national flower, astuteness, thrives upon difficulty.

The miracle follows a Frenchman through life just as it accompanies France throughout her history. The first thing the French (who are cultivated even before they are born) teach their children is that they were found in a cabbage. Parents do everything in their power to make their children become miracle children. As they are brought up in contact with learned spinsters of Sèvres, doting uncles, and philosophic old men, the children of France are very forward for their age and deliver themselves of octogenarian opinions that would drive English parents out of their minds.

The child, openly or in secret, contributes to this devotion of the miracle. He not only learns about Joan of Arc and about the natural frontiers of common sense which the Creator marked out for the French, leaving so many others to discover them for themselves;[1] he associates miracles with those heroes of radio, film, and comic strip who find their way through virgin forests, rescue (English) explorers from certain death, and come back to France with the secret of a mysterious native lethal weapon, and with congratulations from Scotland Yard.

The child learns that, though there may be many countries for earning one's living, France is, after all, the one where life is best spent.

[1] From this point of view, as from so many others, England is, of course, a land apart. Still, I could find no answer to M. Taupin's very strange remark calling my attention to the fact that the first two letters of the word France were those of the English word for liberty—in English (*freedom*), in German (*Freiheit*), in Swedish (*frihet*), in Icelandic (*frelsi*), not to mention other languages—and that all this was a sign of some miraculous order of things. (*Major's note*).

• • •

Land of miracles, miracle men, miracle fashions, realm of Fine Shades and Imponderables, I am about to leave you.

Soon I shall fly off to Bengal at the cordial invitation of my old friend Colonel Basil Cranworth, who, before taking up his new post at Singapore, has asked me to his last Bengal tiger-shoot. But I shall not set off alone, as I used to do. A hundred faces, invisible yet present, escort me. Colonel Cranworth and our host, the Maharajah of Bhagalpur, will not be aware of them, but, while they are talking about man-eaters, Martine's face will hover over the table; I shall think of Martine, and I shall think of Paris. And my longing will not be only sentimental. One evening in India, some months ago now, I felt in the pit of my stomach a nostalgia for France creeping over me. As I slept in my tent in the torrid monsoon-swept jungle of Assam, old Mother Grenouillet appeared to me in a dream: "What are you up to there, Major?" Standing beside the peaceful waters that know neither monsoon nor typhoon, with her hands

"For the kid, a little Saint Emilion after the Montrachet.
That will be lighter . . ."

on her hips, she asked: "What would you say, Major, to some of my trout *à la crème?*"

That night I knew I was a changed man.

Yes, it's done now! Whether I am with the Sikhs or the Zulus, in Rangoon or in Zanzibar, I think of the Place Vendôme and Azay-le-Rideau. And when I come back from India or Kalahari and the airplane, flying over vast reaches of sand and rock where earth and sky seem to have declared war on each other, brings me nearer the winding Seine, over that little hexagon blessed by the gods, where everything is done for man's pleasure on man's scale, for the greater delight of his retina, his palate, and his heart—I know I have come back to the land of miracles.

A land unlike any other, whose farms, churches, and country houses fit so well into the landscape that they all seem to have been born with her.

Land of forty-three million thinking planets, each with its own little idea in the back of its head, whose citizens—all different and all alike in wanting to be different—argue ceaselessly, and in the end conclude: "Fundamentally we agree."

Land where the people's individuality is so pronounced that they cannot hear a weather report without identifying themselves: joyous with "fair weather," and tragic with "stormy."

Strange land, where in one and the same minute I can find someone who detests me and someone who loves me, and realize—and that is the miracle—that they are one and the same person.

Charnelets and Taupins, Turlots and Pochets, all animated by the same spirit of censure and of liberty—I have often spoken ill of you.

Now I must earn your forgiveness.

I have said that you were skeptical, mistrustful, parsimonious. The miracle is that you are also equally enthusiastic, trustful, generous. If tomorrow you were to become disciplined, precise, and silent, a great misfortune would have befallen the world. Your faults are but the reverse side of your virtues. Your nation of foreigner-haters is a refuge for foreigners; you do not abide by the law, yet you bring your children up as strict law-abiders; your people are the most inhospitable in the whole universe, yet your country the most welcoming on the globe. And if it be true that minds are like parachutes (as Lord Dewar said: "To operate, they must be open"), then you are the world's finest parachutists.

Forgive me. Forgive my audacity. Looking back over these notes of an explorer who set out to discover France and the French, I am terrified of my temerity. What right had I, an Englishman, to catalogue your weaknesses? The miserable right of men who think they are qualified to speak about life on earth while they are mere children—a hundred years old or so—when they die. Perhaps simply by that right I learned from Bernard Shaw: the best way to familiarize yourself with a subject is to write a book about it.

It remains for me to obtain forgiveness from my Queen.

That good English governess Miss ffyfth teaches the children of the Bois de Boulogne that they are very lucky to be French, for they inhabit the one country in the world which is only twenty-one miles from England.

May my Sovereign pardon me if I now reverse the axiom: one of the Englishman's privileges is that he need only cross the English Channel to be in France.

May Her Gracious Majesty not hold it against me that I have chosen to live in France. Was it not in my humble way the best I could do to celebrate the Entente Cordiale?

Alas! There is more to come, Your Majesty, and worse. Nowadays I dawdle in the streets of Paris. When a car crashes into another car (and God knows that happens often enough) I stand and stare. Then again—dare I admit it?—such charming silhouettes pass along the Paris streets, especially in spring, that—yes, I find myself turning around. For forty years I saw, now I observe. That is not all: the other day, forgetting all my reserve, I allowed myself to ask M. Taupin about that spot on his nose. And when I left him I said: "*Au revoir, allez!*" Finally, my Queen, there is that terrible longing for snails which may come over me at Gibraltar or in Bombay, or for that Chambolle-Musigny which old Rougetrogne fetches up from his cellar when I go to Avallon, and which brings out the blue line of my temples against the crimson background of my cheeks so marvelously that the *patron* calls to his little boy: "Sonny, come see Major Thompson doing the Union

Jack!" Good Heavens, how disgraceful, Your Majesty!

Meanwhile, I confess: hills of Burgundy, blue reaches of the Île de France, quays of Paris, Saint-Sulpice, Saint-Louis en l'Île, I am your docile slave.

O France, where we can lodge so comfortably and enjoy such delicious meals, how often now have I unfolded your map with its names so full of promise: Brocéliande, Vezelay, Brantôme, Loctudy, where one finds old maids gossiping behind curtains and lovely girls who seem to have been born to give the old maids something to gossip about. France, where one can savor your beautiful days as one savors your food and wine. O France, who offer your goblet and copious horn to the whole world (with a deposit on them). O France! I love your speech, I love your sky, I love your light, I love your stubborn spirit.

I love everything about you and you in everything.

F for folly, *r* for reason, *a* for *amour*, *n* for naughty, *c* for chauvinism, *e* for ever—I love France.

A NOTE ON THE

TYPE

IN WHICH THIS BOOK IS SET

THE TEXT of this book is set in Caledonia, a Linotype face designed by W. A. DWIGGINS. It belongs to the family of printing types called "modern face" by printers—a term used to mark the change in style of type-letters that occurred about 1800. Caledonia borders on the general design of Scotch Modern, but is more freely drawn than that letter.

The book was composed, printed, and bound by H. WOLFF, New York. Paper made by P. H. GLATFELTER CO., Spring Grove, Pa. Typography by SIDNEY R. JACOBS.